The Diary of A.N.

By Julius Horwitz

THE DIARY OF A.N. 1970

THE W.A.S.P. 1967

CAN I GET THERE BY CANDLELIGHT 1964

THE INHABITANTS 1960

THE CITY 1953

The Diary of A.N.

The Story of the House on West 104th Street

JULIUS HORWITZ

Coward-McCann, Inc.
New York

Library of Congress Catalog Card Number: 70–96776

PRINTED IN THE UNITED STATES OF AMERICA

To the memory of my father, Samuel,
and my mother, Jennie

The Diary of A.N.

January 17

We have moved. Momma didn't like the building on 118th Street. Not since Mrs. R was found in the toilet on the fifth floor with her throat cut open. I saw her. It was the first time I had seen a dead person. How unreal the dead look. I asked Momma why we couldn't get an apartment in the projects. She said they wouldn't give it to a family like us on welfare. I learned from A.C. who lives in the projects on 115th Street what a family like us means. A.C. told me that if your mother doesn't have a *real* husband, the project people won't let you in. Does this mean that we have to live forever in a building like the one we moved in? I asked Momma this. But she looks faraway when I talk to her. As though I'm not her child, as though I can't be her child until she can do all of the things a mother is supposed to do. Like buying me dresses fresh and clean instead of bringing them from the Goodwill with all the freshness out of them. Maybe one day we will sit down and talk to one another.

Momma seems to be afraid of words. She won't speak. Maybe it's because there are four of us and she can't speak for a father to.

This is who is in our family. My mother, her name is Esther. My brother Charles, he is 12. My sister Harriet who is 13 and my brother Edgar who is one year and three months. I think I know who is the father of Edgar. But I won't say now.

Then there is me. I am A.N.

January 22

There are enough pages in this diary for me to write something every day. But there isn't something to write every day. We have one room in this building on West 104th Street. On 118th Street we had three rooms. There was no hot water or heat in the building on 118th Street for five weeks. The landlord said the boiler broke and he didn't have money to get it fixed. Momma boiled hot water on the gas stove and we kept the burners going day and night. Momma stuffed up all the windows to keep the heat in but I remembered from school that gas could kill you if you didn't have air and so I always kept one window just a little bit open. Some of the people in the building wanted to kill the landlord. But others said it would do no good.

Momma kept me out of school so that she could go looking for an apartment for us. She went out every morning at nine o'clock and would come home when it was dark. She would be mad and yelling, saying there *had* to be a place in the city for us to live. She said there was no living on West 118th Street. Just cold, fights, screaming people. What Momma says is right but the way we live seems to be all wrong.

January 24

Now I wonder if we should have moved. The cold would have gone away on 118th Street and there we had three rooms. Here on 104th Street we have one room and not even a big room. The room is filled by the two beds where we all sleep, a small refrigerator, a small gas stove. The toilet and bathroom is in the hallway and all the families on this side of the hallway use it. This means 9 families. I counted how many people there are in the 9 families and the number is 47 and with our family it is 52. For two days the toilet was broken. Momma told us to go at school. The bathtub doesn't work in the hall toilet. Momma bought a round plastic tub that we put on the floor and we take a bath with a sponge and hot water.

Momma says we won't stay in this building long. She said it was the only place she could find where they would take five people. Even Edgar is counted as a person. I wish the rats would know this. For the last two nights we have taken turns staying awake to see that none of the rats get to bite Edgar. Momma said we should look for the holes where the rats come from and then we can nail wood or flattened-out tin cans over the holes in the wall. I saw one rat ooze out from under the wall and he came for Edgars crib and I threw the rolled up newspaper Momma gave me at the rat. We had rats on West 118th Street. Harriet woke up one night on 118th Street screaming that something was chewing on the toes of her feet and Momma jumped out of bed and began beating at the rat with a rolled up *Life* magazine.

This building seems to have more rats than all of the buildings that we have lived in that I remember. Maybe it's because of all the people and all the babies. The garbage piles up in all the hallways. Sometimes it's not take down all day. Rats eat garbage. In school they say the way to get rid of rats is to starve them.

January 27

Tonight we located the places where the rats come out and we nailed up the holes. This means Edgar won't get bitten again.

Momma said we can play in the park, Central Park, when it gets warmer. But M.H. told me the park is dangerous. She told me that a man grabbed her in the park and he threw her down and then layed on top of her and then he ran away calling her a dirty black bitch.

February 3

It snowed and snowed. How white the snow is. From our window I can only see a part of the snow. Most of our window looks out on a brick wall. I wish I could see the sky from our window. We have been here almost one month and it seems like forever. I asked Momma who are the people who scream all night? She said I shouldn't talk so much and I should get to sleep. I sleep with Harriet and Charles.

February 5

The snow is gone and the streets are dirty. Momma went to the welfare center on 125th Street to get us money for boots. They didn't give her the money. Momma went over to the Goodwill and brought back three pair of boots. The price is on the bottom of my pair. Fifty cents. The boots have no holes in them and I can walk in the slush.

February 8

Today I went through the entire building. I walked from the first floor to the top floor and I even went out on the roof which Momma said was dangerous. This is what I saw. On the first floor I saw the landlord and landlady of this building. They look like nice people but they keep a filthy building. Is it so hard to get a man to sweep the hallways? I would do it for fifty cents. The landlord and the landlady stay in a tiny room in front of the building. There is a big piece of chicken wire across the opening to the room where the people pay their rent. The door to the room is always locked. The landlord and the landlady wear old clothes. Maybe this is to make them look poor. But they take so much money in rent. Momma pays $21.95 a week for our one room. The landlady is always screaming at somebody even when she tries to talk softly. She always complains that somebody is taking something from her, when she is always the one who is doing the taking. She keeps a pile of old clothes in the front room and she sells the clothes to the people in the building. She lends money to the people in the building and they give her two dollars if she gives them a dollar. But she is the only person who will lend money to anybody. This is what Momma told me. The landlord looks like a nice man. He looks sick most of the time. There is a sad look on his face. Momma heard that he couldn't work anymore at his job and he took his savings and bought this house. Now he sits in the room like a prisoner. It is like a jail. The drunken men scream at him but nobody hits him or hurts him because he is the only friend any one can have here when they run out of money, which is very often.

I have no friends on the first floor. Mostly old people live on the first floor. They don't speak to anyone. I see them through the open doors of their rooms. Their rooms are smaller than ours. It seems there is only space for a bed and a chair. Most of the time they lay on their beds. The walls to their rooms are covered with cockroaches. They don't have the strength to get off their beds to kill the cockroaches. The cockroaches crawl on the walls, the beds, the sink, over the old people.

The landlady wanted to give me a blouse but it was dirty and I wouldn't take it. I need clothes but I don't dare tell Momma. You wear welfare clothes, Clara Brown yelled at me in the hallway of our school. I grabbed her arm and twisted it. She said, I'll get you. I twisted it harder and she started to cry. She ran away from me calling out again, You wear welfare clothes!

February 10

What is welfare? I asked my teacher. She told me she didn't have time to discuss it. My homeroom teacher in this new school is an Irish lady, Mrs. L. She looks about 55. I have other teachers but I seem to spend a lot of my time with Mrs. L. When I asked Mrs. L., What is welfare? her face got very hard. She looked at me the way I look at the cockroaches crawling over the old people on 104th Street. She wouldn't talk to me. She seems to hate welfare the way the other people hate welfare. Is welfare something you are born into, like the serfs were born into being serfs in the middle ages? Are you born in this world into what you are and stay as you are? I thought from my history books that you grew into what you are as a person and a lot depended on you. But what part of life doesn't depend on what you *do* but what happens to you outside of yourself? That is the scary part. The whole world working for you or against you.

Momma just won't talk to me about welfare. I tried to get her to tell me just how she got started on welfare. But she turned away and told me to get in front of the TV.

It seems that I have been on welfare all of my life. I can't remember any other time of my life when there wasn't welfare.

I think welfare is bad. But I don't understand why it should be bad. Is welfare a punishment? Is Momma being punished for what she did when she was a girl almost as old as I am now? Is that what welfare is, a punishment for doing something bad in your life? So that all money is taken away from you and the only money you are permitted to get comes in the check figured to the last penny? The check that comes once every two weeks that everybody hates but that no one refuses.

Momma immediately takes the check and pays the landlord. With the money that is left she takes me and Harriet to the A&P and we buy all the food we can. Then Momma gives us each 15 cents. I buy two chocolate bars because the chocolate bars are now 6 cents. Momma says that if you don't spend the check money immediately for food then the money vanishes. Momma has to leave some money over for the laundermat. And sometimes we need money for school. Momma says the check money doesn't give us any extra money left over for the movies, toys, games, books, but sometimes she does have money left over for me and Harriet to go to the movies.

When did welfare begin? I finally got one of my teachers to talk to me, Miss A., who is younger than most of my teachers. She is my English teacher. Miss A. said that people always helped other people who ran out of money, mostly the sick and the very old. A long time ago they were put into institutions, together with widows and their children. Miss A. said the institutions were terrible places with mean people in charge and the food was terrible and the babies died of starvation and the old people died of hunger and the widows just grew into wasted old ladies. They were called poorhouses and you went there almost like a prisoner went to jail. You lived there like a prisoner. There was no private life for yourself. There was no escape but to die. Everybody slept in big rooms and sometimes on the floor. The poorhouse was known to everybody in town and that was the place you went to if you didn't work hard, if you failed in life, if you grew old without any money or children to look after you. Miss A. said the poorhouses were terrible and some people thought it would be a better idea to give people money and to let them live in their own homes and buy their own food and look after themselves. The government would give them just enough money to live on, no more no less. This Miss A. said was the beginning of welfare. She said President Roosevelt was the president who made up the new laws about welfare.

I do not believe that the government in Washington knows what welfare is.

February 14

I made a Valentine for Momma in school today. The art teacher said that all the children who didn't have money to buy a Valentine could make one in school. She meant all the children on welfare.

February 19

There was a banging on our door last night. We all woke up. Momma said, Don't open the door. Momma got up and put a chair against the door knob. A mans voice said, Let me in. Momma said, Go away. The mans voice said, Let me in or I'll break down the door. Momma cried out again, Go away. Another voice yelled out, Stop that banging or I'll bang your head in. It was Mr. G. Everybody knows he is a drug addict. The man banging on the door went away. I think I recognized his voice. He is the father of Edgar.

February 22

Momma hasn't gone out in a week to look for a new place to live. I hope she isn't getting used to this place.

February 25

I found out today that every apartment in this building only has one room. Why didn't they make two room apartments when they broke up the big apartments that used to be here? Across the street they did that and the rent is $30 a week. I went to visit a girl friend, P.K., there. At first she didn't want me to come to her house. I think she was ashamed for me to see how she lived. But when she learned I was on welfare it made it all right.

The front door to her building is smashed. The super was nailing pieces of wood where the glass used to be. The hallways are dark. The paint is green and there is writing on the walls. The steps are dirty. You can smell what everybody is cooking. All the TVs seem to be going at the same time. P.K. lives on the 4th floor. The door to her house opens right into the toilet. The door almost touches the toilet. You have to squeeze past the kitchen to get into the living room. A folding bed was in the small hallway. The living room was hot. All the windows were closed. The TV was going even though nobody was looking at it. P.K. has five brothers and sisters. They sleep in the back room. I went into the back room with P.K. The walls were broken. The one window was broken and there was cardboard and a bed sheet over it because the blind was also broken. There was a bunk bed in the room and a torn couch that opened into a double bed. There was one chest and the drawers were pulled out. There was a big pile of clothing in one corner. P.K. said her mother saves all the clothing to give from one child to another. I saw cockroaches on the walls. They were big and didn't seem to be afraid of us. P.K. and myself sat on the edge of the bunk bed. There were no chairs in the room. P.K. said to me, Do you have rats? I said we had but we nailed up most of the holes. P.K. asked me how we did it. I told her that we waited to see where the rats came from and then we put pieces of wood or tin cans over the holes. P.K. asked me where we got the hammer. I said we just had the hammer. P.K. said she would try and get a hammer and some nails. She said the rats and mice were terrible at night. I noticed that she fell asleep in class. The homeroom teacher, Mrs. L., always screams at her. Wake up! Wake up! she cries at P.K. and P.K. sits up in her seat not knowing what to do except to try and look awake. I told P.K. that I would let her use our hammer and nails and I would help her nail up the holes. The same landlord owns the two buildings. Isn't he supposed to nail up the holes? I wish Momma would ask such questions. I can only think them.

On the steps later on P.K. told me that I was the first person to ever see her house. She said they had been living on 104th Street for two years. P.K. said she figured out that her mother pays from her welfare check $120 a month rent or $1440 a year and in two years it was $2880. For *that*, P.K. said, pointing upstairs.

On the stoop P.K. told me that she wanted to be a nurse.

February 27

P.K. and myself went for a walk. We can never be friends. I felt this as we walked. We have too much to hide from one another. Maybe this is why Momma has no friends among the women who are on welfare. But the walk was nice. We went away from 104th Street walking along Riverside Drive. We came to a place where boats were anchored in the river. We went down to the boats. They moved in the cold water as though ready to break away. They looked so white and clean. The white paint was more white than any white paint I'd ever seen. We saw one boat with shining brass everywhere. We went down a ramp that led to the boats. No one stopped us. P.K. and myself both looked up at one another as we came to the end of the ramp. Where could we sail? What shores could we go to? What would take us on our own voyage? P.K. said when we got back on Broadway, Those were the first boats I ever saw that weren't on TV.

March 3

Momma lost her welfare check. A gang of five boys broke into our room when the door was open. They all had knives. They took Mommas check. The gang went from room to room taking checks from the old people. Nobody could fight them back. The police came two hours after they left. The Sergeant told Momma that the welfare office would give her a new check if she reported that her check had been taken from her by the gang. The gang took fifteen checks. They cut Mr. Downs on the 5th floor. The ambulance came faster than the police.

March 11

I went with Momma to the welfare center on 125th Street today. Momma said I could help her tell the story to the welfare investigator so that we could get our money. Momma gets excited whenever she has to go to the welfare center. It makes her nervous. She almost lost the note the detective gave her. It fell and started to blow away. I ran after it. She said nobody would believe the money was taken from her without the note.

We have to ride the freight elevator on 124th Street to get to the reception desk. The reception floor looks gloomy. All the people are sitting and waiting for money because they have no money. It is a terrible place. You sit and wait for your name to be called out if the investigator doesn't know your face. Mommas investigator always asks the old questions. Momma hates to repeat the old answers over and over again. This makes her angry. Mommas name was called out and this time the investigator was a black girl. She looked about 25. She stared at Momma and Momma stared at her. Momma could have been an investigator if she had gone to college. But Momma had a baby before she could get to college. Momma finished high school. Her mother kept the baby at home so that Momma could go to classes. The investigator asked Momma how she lost her check. Momma repeated the story about the gang coming into the rooms on 104th Street with knives and stealing the checks. The investigator said, Where were the police? Momma looked at her like she was one of those black people who have forgotten they were once black. The police came later, Momma said. I could see Momma was keeping back, trying not to yell and shout, which is the only way you get attention in the reception room. The investigator said to me, Did you see the gang? I said yes. The investigator said to me, What did they look like? I said there were five of them and they all had knives and I didn't know any of them. Momma took out the note from the police. The investigator looked at the note. She asked Momma if the police caught any of the gang. Momma said the police were afraid of the gang because the gang killed people. Momma told the investigator that our landlord offered the police $200 if they would stay in the building on check days just to catch the gang but the police said no. The landlord is afraid that they will kill him. The investigator said, Why don't you move? Momma said, Do you have any rooms that I can move into? The investigator said, You know we have a shortage of rooms, you have to find it yourself. Momma said, What about my check? The investigator said, I have to go upstairs and make out a new emergency check. You'll have to wait. It will take some time.

We waited for three hours. Momma was ready to start screaming. The black ones make you wait, Momma said. Black against black, Momma said. The reception room was filled with people, all sitting on the chairs and benches, some of them going into little rooms to talk to the investigators.

I have the feeling that this is a place I never want to come to when I grow up.

At four o clock the investigator came over to Momma. Here's your check, the investigator said. Don't lose this one. Momma said, I didn't lose it. The investigator said if you lose to many checks they can't be replaced. The supervisor won't sign for the checks. Momma said you tell your supervisor to tell his supervisor to tell his supervisor to tell his supervisor about the gang on 104th Street so that maybe the police will do something.

The investigator said to Momma, I'm not your investigator, and walked away. Momma said, Son of a bitch.

We took the freight elevator down to 124th Street. I asked Momma why they gave her a new check.

Momma said, Because we only have checks to live on for every 15 days and we have no other money, nothing in the bank, nothing in the house, nothing in my pocketbook. So if our money is taken from us, they have to replace it because you cant live without money in New York City, even if you are on welfare.

March 19

F.P. was thrown out of school today. She is pregnant. She is six months younger than me. I know who the father is. He is D.N. F.P. told us that she is in her 5th month. It doesn't show on her. She could have stayed in class until her 8th month.

March 21

When I came home from school there was a man laying on the sidewalk. He looked like Mr. Williams from the 2nd floor, two doors from our room. His body was moving around on the sidewalk. About 20 people were watching him. Somebody said he took to much dope. Nobody did anything for him.

When the ambulance came they took him away. Today in English class the teacher, Miss A., asked us to write an essay on what we know about drugs. The boys in the class laughed out loud when she said that was our assignment. F. stood up and started jabbing a pencil in his arm. P. went around the room sniffing from his hand into his nose. The boys all started jabbing their arms with pencils. Miss A. yelled out to stop it. P. fell down on the floor and started twitching the same way the man twitched on the sidewalk. Miss A. started screaming for everybody to sit down. The principal walked into the room. He yelled out for everybody to be quiet. He asked Miss A. what was going on. But Miss A. was crying. I'm afraid she will leave this school. This morning when we walked into the classroom there was written on the board, Miss A. sucks.

March 22

Miss A. was out and we had a sub.

March 28

The substitute teacher ran out of the room today when A.H. threw a steel-tipped dart at B.D. The steel-tipped darts are something new. The boys whip them out of their pockets and throw them at each other. The trick is to duck very fast. The darts stick on the desks and the floor. Nobody has been hit yet in the eye. I miss Miss A. She tries to get us to do some work in class. With the subs nothing gets done. They just come in for the money and hang around until 3 o'clock.

April 1

Mommas investigator came to 104th Street today for the first time. Mommas investigator is a man about 35 years old. He is white. He puffs when he comes into the room. He can't climb stairs. He holds on tight to a black notebook. The black notebook is supposed to protect him. Nobody is supposed to beat up the investigators because they bring money. But this isn't always true. Mr. E. in room 804 says he is going to kill a welfare investigator before he gets off of welfare. Mr. E. only has one leg and he is drunk all the time. I don't see how he will ever get off welfare.

Mommas investigator is Mr. C. He wears a sport jacket and his pants are never pressed. Most of the time he needs a haircut. His face is flushed. This is from walking the stairs. Even though we live on the 2nd floor the steps are steep.

Momma gave Mr. C. the chair. He looked first to see if any cockroaches were crawling on it. He stepped on one that ran past his foot and he knocked one off the table. Momma told Harriet to go around killing the roaches. Mr. C. opened his black notebook. The first thing he said was, Can I see your rent receipt? Mr. C. was on vacation when Momma moved and then we weren't due for a visit until now. The investigator is supposed to come to your house once every three months. Mr. C. said, Are you paying $20 a week for this room? Momma said, I had to move. Mr. C. said, Was this the only place for you to move in? Momma said yes. Mr. C. said, Are you planning to move out? Momma said, If I can find another place. Have you got one? she asked. Mr. C. said he would check to see. He said, You can't have five people living in one room, it's against the law. Momma said, I couldn't stay on 118th Street. Mr. C. said, This is a rough building. Momma said, It just looks dirtier than the others but it's no different. Mr. C. then began to tell Momma what he always tells her, Why don't you move to Brooklyn? You can rent the bottom half of a private house for the money you pay here, you can't find anything or anyplace to live in Manhattan, it's to crowded, to filled up with people on welfare who need more than one room. Momma said, I don't know anyone in Brooklyn. Mr. C. said, Who do you know here? Momma said, I grew up in Manhattan. Mr. C. said, So your children can grow up in Brooklyn. Momma said, You find me a place in Brooklyn and I'll go out and see it, I can't go looking anymore, every place I see is dirtier than the next place. Don't you tell anyone at that center about the filth? Momma asked. You people pay the rent. Mr. C. said he would report the garbage in the hallways. Momma said that the landlord gives the building inspector fifty dollars every time he comes. Mr. C. said he would report the building as dangerous. Momma said, That won't do any good.

Mr. C. asked Momma if she saw the father of Edgar. Momma said, I don't see him and I don't want to see him. Mr. C. said, He has to support his son. Momma said, He couldn't support a fly. Momma said she hasn't seen the father of Edgar in three months. This is a lie. The father of Edgar was in bed with Momma two nights ago. Momma put Edgar in our bed so they would have room. We could all hear Momma and Edgar's father. Momma said to him during the night, Don't you come here any more, if they get an investigator here at night then they'll throw me off welfare. He left before the morning. Where does he sleep and how does he live? He never looks at Edgar. He never brought Edgar a toy. He just comes to be in bed with Momma. If Momma has another baby there will be another Edgar in the world without a father to look at him.

Mr. C. asked Momma if she needed anything. Momma said, I need spring coats for the two girls and a jacket for Charles. Mr. C. wrote it down in his black book.

Mr. C. closed his notebook. He stood up and looked around the room. He saw there was no place for us to sit down and eat. He saw the beds took up most of the room. Mr. C. stepped on another cockroach and then he left.

April 3

The landlord had a scare today. Mr. L. from the top floor threw a bottle against the chicken wire because the landlord would not give him two dollars.

April 7

Miss A. is back. I hope she will stay. She didn't start yelling or screaming until two boys started throwing the darts at each other. She picked up the darts and said, Darts is an old English game and when you're in England you can use them but not in my classroom.

April 8

I went into Central Park today for the first time. Momma told us to stay out of the park. But I saw other people walking around. The sun was out. The grass is getting green. There is a big rock on West 104th Street but it looks to dangerous to climb. I just went far enough in the park to put my feet on the grass and then I ran back to 104th Street.

April 14

Charles is in trouble at school. The teacher said she is going to keep him out of the classes. Momma said she can't do that. But the school can. There is a boy on our floor who was kept out of school. The teachers all made a complaint against him. They said they couldn't do anything to keep him. He had a regular trial and the principal said he should stay at home from 9 to 3, which are the school hours. He is not supposed to leave this house. But from 9 to 3 the drunks are in all the hallways and they fight and scream. I haven't talked to the boy but I see him by his door when I come home from school. He lives with his grandmother who is an old Puerto Rican woman almost 75. They have a tiny room and he sleeps with her. I never see anyone come to visit them. The boy is getting fatter than when I first saw him. He stares at you as if you don't have a face to stare back at him.

April 16

Mrs. L. my homeroom teacher quit the school.

April 22

If I don't write in my diary every day it is because some days are to terrible to write about.

April 24

Momma hasn't gone out in two weeks to look for a new place to live. The toilet is still broken on our floor. I get so stiff from trying to hold everything in. Harriet went to use the one on the 3rd floor and a man followed her into the toilet. She screamed and Mr. R. came running into the toilet and he threw the man out. The toilet is broken on the 4th floor to. I go in school but the toilet in school is filled with girls who try to stick their hands inside of your pants. Now I carry a bottle opener with me. I learned that from Momma. The girls who hang out in the toilet have parties where they get drunk and some take drugs. They make love like boys. I heard one of them say, It's better than getting it from a boy and then going on welfare with a little bastard. All this is in our school. I don't believe it happens in all schools.

April 27

It is 3 months since I have taken a real bath. The bathtub on our floor is stopped up. There is plaster in the bathtub and old newspapers that are wet. The plaster has fallen down from the ceiling. The hot water doesn't come out. The lock on the toilet door is always broken. I wrote a letter to the Dept. of Buildings from a story that I saw in the newspaper. But no one has come to fix the bathtub. I ask Momma to call her investigator every day to see if he can get her an apartment where we can have our own room and our own toilet and bathtub. Momma doesn't seem to want to move from here. I learned today that some people have been living in this building for two and three years.

I talked to K.H. on the top floor today. She is one year older than me. She lives in room 509 with her mother, one brother and one sister. There is no place in their room to walk. She moved in two years and eight months ago. I asked her why they didn't move out. She said her mother couldn't find an apartment where they would take four people. I told her they took four people across the street in the two room apartments I saw. She said no, the welfare people would only let you move in there if there were 5 people in your family. I said we were 5 in our family. She said, If somebody moves out then you can move in. K.H.s mother sits in her room all day. She says she can't walk down the stairs. K.H. does all the shopping. K.H. told me she is going to get a baby and get her own welfare check and find her own place to live.

April 29

I haven't had any homework in three weeks, except for English. The subs don't give homework because they think no one will do the homework. We had a different sub every day for a week.

I started to read *Robinson Cruso*. I think he had it easier than this house.

May 3

The investigator came again today. He sat down in the chair puffing from the walk up the stairs. He never talks to me or Harriet. I don't think he sees us. Maybe he doesn't want to see us living all in one room. He opened his black book. Momma couldn't figure out why he had come back so soon. Momma looked worried, as though someone had told the investigator that Edgar's father was coming to the room. They must know that at night the house on West 104th Street is filled with men who come into the rooms. The men are gone in the morning. I see them going off when I go to school. How do I go to school? I put some water on my face. The towel is always wet and dirty. I like the smell of hot fresh towels. I take some milk from the refrigerator and I pour it on cornflakes and I always pray that there are not any cockroaches in the cornflakes. If there are cockroaches, I don't eat the cornflakes, even if I am hungry. I can't eat the free lunch at school even if the food sometimes smells good because everybody calls it welfare food. But sometimes I have to eat it because there is nothing else.

Momma waited to see what the investigator was going to read from his black book. The investigator asked Momma if she filled out an application for the projects. Momma said it wouldn't do any good. The investigator said it wasn't up to Momma to say so. He said he couldn't get her any apartment until she filled out an application for the projects even if they wouldn't accept her. He said that was a rule. Momma said she would go to the project office and get an application. The investigator told Momma that he tried to get an apartment for her but the housing advisor at the welfare office didn't have any apartments to give out. The investigator told Momma that she would have to keep looking. He told Momma that other women found apartments. Momma got mad. She said she goes out every day.

The investigator then began to say something that made me feel weak in my legs like I would never walk again. He told Momma, there are some women who get used to buildings like this, they go on living here year after year and the more dirty everything becomes, the more the women like it because then they have an excuse for everything. I kept watching Momma to see if she was listening. I was listening. But Momma got mad. She said to the investigator, Why can't they keep a building like this clean? The investigator said, This building is meant to be dirty, it exists to be dirty, it takes in people nobody else will take in, it's a dumping ground for the welfare office. Maybe you didn't know that when you moved in, but I'm telling you that now, this building is nothing more than a dumping ground for people who nobody else will take in, that's why this building isn't closed down, why everybody protects it and why the landlord can get away with charging you $20 a week. The investigator got up from his chair. He said to Momma, Fill out the application, maybe you can tell some lies on it, maybe you can get a marriage certificate somewhere or some birth certificates. It's worth it to get into a project. If you get an apartment in a project I can give you money to buy a house full of new furniture. Even if you find an apartment on your own I can give you the money to buy all the furniture you need to set up your own house. You have to keep looking and looking. If you stop looking, then you've only got this. When the investigator left I asked Momma what she thought of what he said. Momma said, He can talk, he's got his place waiting for him.

Momma never talked this way before.

May 4

Momma was mad when the investigator went. Talk, talk, talk, she said, Jesus when will they stop talking and do something? Like burn this building down, Harriet said. Momma slapped Harriet across the face for saying it. This is where you live now, Momma yelled at Harriet, this is where you make your life now. Harriet went out into the hallway.

Momma yelled at me to open a can of vegetable and beef soup for dinner. If we eat soup for dinner we eat it out of cups and we don't have to sit down to a plate. Momma bought a little folding table at the Goodwill that we use now for eating. It has to be folded up afterwards because there is no place for it. I unfold it sometimes when I have to do homework.

I am halfway through reading *Robinson Cruso.* I wonder what he would do with this house? He would sleep in Central Park rather than this room. With the warm weather coming the smells are terrible. The smell of frying pork makes me sick. Harriet is starting to have asthma attacks. She wakes up unable to breathe. It scares Momma. Edgar to has trouble breathing at night. Momma said she is going to buy some chicken wire and put it over the windows. The screens are no good. Anybody can lift out the screens and steal what you have in the room. If you leave your door unlocked something will be taken. Mrs. W. from 305 came screaming down the hallway saying her TV set had been stolen from her room. The police will never be able to find it. You are not supposed to have a TV set if you are on welfare but most people do. Momma pays $5 a week out of her welfare check for ours. If you miss a payment Momma says they start from the beginning and charge you all over again. If you miss more than one payment they sometimes come and take the set away. Momma says she will chop the arms off of anybody who tries to take our set away after all the payments she made on it. She has now made 25 payments or $125. I saw the same TV set in a store window for $98 and Momma has 20 more payments to make.

May 7

I asked Momma to tell me her history today. She told me to run to the store and get a container of milk for Edgar.

May 11

Edgar's father was in the room when I came home from school today. He is a tall thin man and he has a scar around his neck which means somebody once cut him. Momma has a faint scar on her face near her neck but she won't tell me where it came from. I don't know the name of Edgar's father. He doesn't say much. He sits on the chair and stares at Momma. Today he was drinking from a bottle of wine. He told Momma that the investigator had found out where he lives. He asked Momma if she told the investigator. Momma said no. Edgar's father said, You must have told him, now he wants me to sign a paper or go to court. Now they'll be after me, he said. Momma said he should sign the paper. Then I'll be his father, he said. Momma said, Don't be afraid to say his name, you'll be Edgar's father. Edgar's father said to Momma, Shut up, you bitch. It's your baby, Momma said. You say it, I don't, he said. Momma said, Don't talk about it anymore. Edgar's father said, That god damn investigator will be back to my room, he has my social security number now. Momma said, They only ask you to give a little money for Edgar. He said, I don't have a little money, I just got enough for me. Then you have to get some more, Momma said. He said, Not from me. Momma said, Then don't sign the paper, Edgar doesn't need you for a father, you just don't know how to be a father. Momma went over to the bed and put Edgar in front of his father. Pick up your baby, Momma said, hold him in your arms once, just once, look at his face, feel him breathing, wash one of his diapers, smell his shit, get to know him, get to know that more comes out of your p. than just white stuff, you made a human life you miserable nigger, now get out of here, don't come here telling me about investigators, I've got them coming out of my teeth. Edgar's father got to the door and he turned to Momma and said, You got four fathers for your four bastards, and he went.

Momma turned to me and said, Don't listen to a man like that, don't listen.

May 15

Momma still hasn't gone out to look for a new apartment. When I talk to her about it she tells me to shut up. Something must be bothering Momma that she won't talk about.

May 17

Charles is out of school. He has to stay in the room from 9 to 3. Momma is mad. She went to the school and yelled at the principal. Charles stays in bed all morning. Momma caught him smoking cigarettes and she cracked him in the face.

Do we make up a family, Momma, Harriet, Charles, Edgar and myself?

May 20

Harriet told me she has a boy friend.

May 22

A new man was in our room tonight. Momma didn't tell us his name. He didn't leave after we went to sleep. He went into Momma's bed. I could hear them for about an hour. Then they were quiet. He was gone when we woke up. Momma made hot tea for Harriet and me. Charles was sleeping. Edgar was crying. My dress was to dirty to wear to school but there was nothing else ready. Harriet's dresses won't fit me. She is tall and thin and looks 16. Our clothes are beginning to pile up like I see the clothes in some of the other rooms in this building. That's because we only have one chest for all of us. The drawers on the chest are broken, they won't slide shut and all the clothes stick out. Momma put some nails on the wall to hang up our dresses. Our room now is beginning to look like everybody elses room. Dirty with clothes piled up. The dishes stay dirty in the sink. The investigator can give us a new chest of drawers but there is no place in the room for a chest. The investigator can give us dishes but we don't have a place to keep the dishes. Momma must find a place to live. We must find a room where we can all sit down to supper and where everything will be so clean the roaches will be afraid to come out. But Momma seems to like it here. She talks to more of the women. They are all on welfare. Every single person in this building is on welfare. Every single person in the house across the street is on welfare. And in the two houses next to it, every single person is on welfare. Maybe we shouldn't see so many welfare people. But this whole street is welfare.

When I walk to Broadway it's easy to see a welfare building. The men are sitting outside on the stoop and they do nothing but talk and nobody listens. The women sit by the windows. They look out. I don't want to see Momma's face get like their faces. They see nothing, like the men. When I get to Broadway there is more welfare. I took a walk with D.L. She told me she lived in eight different buildings on Broadway between 96th Street and 110th Street and they were all welfare buildings. I don't believe you, I said. D.L. took me into a building on 107th Street. We went to the second floor and I saw rows and rows of garbage cans and long hallways and rooms. The walls were dirty, with writing on them. D.L. showed me the other buildings she lived in. They look so nice from the outside. Does anybody on the sidewalk know about the buildings they pass? On 101st Street, D.L. took me up a narrow stairway and we went past the open doors where old people were laying on mattresses without bedsheets. Some of the old people tried to smile at us. One old lady looked like she was dead. She was so stiff and so thin but then she began to cough. D.L. said to me, We only stayed here two days, my mother rushed over to the welfare office and she said if they didn't give her another room she was going to throw me out of the window and she ran over to the window with me and a policeman there grabbed my mother. Maybe this is why Momma's investigator talks so much about Brooklyn.

May 27

Momma was screaming. She found some marks on Charles arm. Charles said he was only playing. Playing where? Momma screamed. On the roof, Charles said. Who had the needle? Momma screamed. A friend, Charles said. Was there anything in the needle? Momma yelled at Charles. Nothing, Charles said. You were supposed to stay in the room, Momma screamed at Charles. I went out for a minute, Charles said. To the roof, Momma said, I told you to stay off that roof. We were playing, Charles said. I'll find out if you were playing, Momma said. She took Charles arm and started to wash away the marks and they wouldn't go away.

Momma sat down on a chair and started pounding her hands against her head.

How long, she asked Charles, how long have you been sticking the needles in your arm?

Charles didn't answer.

Momma said, Speak or I'll kill you now. She slapped Charles across his face. Charles still didn't say a word.

Momma said, Who gave you the needle?

Charles didn't say a word.

Momma slapped Charles again. He ran away from her and went into a corner of the room crouching down like a sick animal.

Momma said, I'll beat you with this broom.

Charles finally said, I can't tell you anything.

Momma cried out, You'll tell the police.

Charles said, I won't do it again.

How many times did you do it? Momma asked.

Charles said, Five times.

Since when? Momma asked.

Since I stayed out of school.

How did it happen? Momma asked.

I went up to the roof, Charles said. Three other boys were there. They called me over. One of them said, Did you ever do this? He showed me a needle. I said, No. He said, Do you want to? I said, I don't know. He said, Do you know what it is? I said I saw the men on the 3rd floor sticking a needle into their arm and I saw it done in the toilet on our floor by two girls who thought nobody was watching them. Do you know what it does? they asked me. I said no. They said, Happy. Do you want to be happy? I said, Happy about what? That made them crack up. One of them said, Roll up your sleeve. I said, You're no doctor. They cracked up again. Then one of the boys brushed the needle against my arm. He said, This costs money, do you have any money? I said I had a quarter. They reached into my pocket and took the quarter. They said, Do you have any money in your room? I said, No. They said, Do you have a radio? I said, No. They said, How come you're at home? I said, The school said I should stay at home. They said, We'll give you this free. The next one costs. We're up here everyday. Only you got to look for us because we don't know who's looking for us. Then one of the boys stuck the needle in me. I didn't feel anything for a minute except it hurt where the needle went in. Then I felt I was going to sleep only I wasn't sleeping. Then I felt the boys on the roof were my friends for life. Then I tried to sit down but I wanted to stand. I felt I was as tall as the trees. Then I heard them laughing and they ran over to the next roof. When I got to the next roof I couldn't see them. I went off the roof and got into bed and went to sleep.

Oh Jesus, Momma said.

Maybe now we'll move.

May 29

Now I know how much money we get from welfare. Momma left a budget letter on the table that the investigator sent. Momma gets $18.95 every two weeks. Charles gets $23.70. Harriet and myself get $21.65 each and Edgar gets $12.65. This is for food and clothing. It totals $98.60. We also get rent money and some money for the laundermat, $4.90. How do they figure out everything to the penny? How do they know I need $21.65 every two weeks to live? Momma only gives me $.25 of the $21.65. I wonder if other families figure out their money this way. When a man works does he say so much is for this child and so much for that child, or does all the money go for the *family?*

Are we a family?

May 30

Today is a holiday. No school. But everyday seems like no school. In history, science, math, the teachers yell and scream and try to keep the boys quiet. For every boy they send out of the room another one starts up. Sometimes we can't resist and we all join in yelling and screaming at the teachers. Two days ago I was screaming at the top of my voice. Then I heard what I was screaming. I was screaming, *I want to learn, I want to learn.* Did the teachers hear me? Miss A., my English teacher, is the only teacher I talk to. She is white. She wears her hair long. She dresses almost like a high school girl. She doesn't look as if she has been out of high school very long. Her voice is quiet. The boys won't let her alone. When she tries to tell us something the boys begin to drum on the desks with their fingers. One day in class I couldn't stand it and I stood up and shouted, Cut it out, cut it out. The boys started laughing and rolling on the floor and it was worse than it was before. Are the boys afraid of learning? Are they frightened of what they don't know? Do new words make them angry? Most of them can't speak their own language. They talk in grunts and use a handful of words that they think makes them superior to everybody else. But instead it just hides what they don't know. They never bother taking a test in class. They never open a book. Instead of looking at the teacher they stare at each other or out of the window. Some of them get taken out of class to go to a 600 school which is like a reformatory. There is one on 93rd Street. They say the toughest boys go there.

I don't think they are so tough. I think they are all like Charles. Hiding under the bedsheets, trying to cover up under the blankets. They are afraid of their own shadows. They are afraid of themselves, just like Charles is afraid. That is why he is so bold in bed. He put his hands on my breasts last night and started rubbing them, but I stopped him and then he turned to Harriet. I think Harriet waits now for Charles to touch her. I can hear Harriet breathing even though she tries to keep quiet. If Momma saw this she would find a room where we could have bunk beds or two more beds. Charles needs his own bed.

Momma makes Charles promise everyday that he won't go to the roof. I can see that she doesn't know what to do about Charles and the boys who made him stick drugs in his arm the way the men do on this block.

I went into Central Park today with my girl friend, P.L. She lives on 109th Street. This is the block where most of the drug addicts are supposed to be. But it looks so nice from the outside. Better than 104th Street. We walked together in Central Park. P. L. wants to be a lawyer. She told me about a black woman lawyer she read about who makes $55,000 a year. She was on welfare once, P.L. told me. Welfare wouldn't be so bad, P.L. said, if they just let you be. P.L. told me her mother is a drug addict. She said her mother does it quietly, nobody else in her family knows about it. P.L. told me her mother brings men into the room and charges them mostly $5 and this way she has enough money to pay for the drugs she has to use. P.L. said to me, I heard my mother tell a neighbor, it's like a medicine, I need it to keep alive. Then why don't they give it to my mother like a medicine? she said. This is what we talked about in Central Park. P.L. said that the man who sells the drugs to her mother is the super of her building. P.L. has five rooms. P.L. said sometimes her mother has five men a day, then everybody has to be out of the house and into the street. P.L. told me she followed her mother one day to see how she does her business. P.L. said her mother just walked along Broadway very slow and if a man looked at her she walked slower and she waited for the man to come up to her. Then they talked for a few minutes and if everything was all right she brought the man back. P.L. said her mother can sometimes make more money in one day than they get in their welfare check, but her mother needs the money to give to the super for drugs.

I wonder if Momma has ever done this.

June 1

Momma asked me today if I wanted to go to the Goodwill store on 124th Street with her. Momma hardly ever asks me to go anywhere with her except to the A&P so I said all right, even if I don't like the Goodwill. Momma said some women spend their whole lives at the Goodwill, always hoping to find a bigger and better bargain, even if the clothes are all cast off. The Goodwill is a dream for them, Momma said, but no matter what expensive clothes those women put on from the Goodwill bins, it always looks like rags on them. But the Goodwill excites Momma to. She said one day she will find a sweater with one of those fur collars there, which is what she has always wanted. Maybe any other man but Edgar's father would have bought Momma the sweater long ago.

Momma always gets excited as we get nearer to the Goodwill store, even if we have to go past the addicts on 125th Street and Park Avenue who stand asleep on their feet, swaying but never falling because I think they must know there is nobody to catch them. In the Goodwill store which is a big store with racks of worn dresses and worn coats, racks of old shoes and bins of worn blouses, worn underwear, worn sweaters, scarves, Momma rushed to the bin with the babys clothing to see what she could find for Edgar. Momma gave me a dollar and said I could go into the bookstore. A tall thin lady was in the bookstore who looked as though her one arm was paralyzed and she had difficulty speaking. But she smiled at me when I came in. She said some new childrens books were just brought in in the carton on the floor. I went to the carton and picked out three big Golden books for Edgar. There was a Golden book dictionary of eight books and she said I could have the whole set for 25 cents. She said I could have all the Golden books I could carry for 50 cents. She asked me if I read a lot. I said I tried to read three books a week. She said reading kept her alive when she had her first operation. She asked me if I knew that everyone who worked in the Goodwill store was physically handicapped in some way. I said, No. She said they were very handicapped and probably couldn't get a job anywhere else but at the Goodwill. You look at the books, she said to me, don't let my talking interfere with your looking, sometimes you see a book in the racks here that is just right for you that you never expected to find or dreamt existed. I told her I would take the Golden books for my brother Edgar and she got out a shopping bag to make the books easier to carry. I went to the racks of books as though I was in a library. I saw a lot of familiar titles I had read already and books that had become movies like the *Caine Mutiny*. There was a beautiful bible with a leather binding and gold letters. I asked her how much the bible was so I could buy it for Momma. She said she didn't *sell* the bibles and I could have it for free because she didn't believe in selling bibles but gave them to whoever showed an interest. That seemed to me like one of the most wonderful things I had ever heard in my life.

The Golden books, the dictionaries and the bible filled the shopping bag. She asked me if I wasn't going to buy any books for myself. I saw a lot of books that I wanted but I only bought two of them, for which she charged me a nickel a piece. I bought the *Arabian Nights* and a thick old leather book that has every word Shakespeare ever wrote. Momma helped me carry the books. Momma bought Edgar two sweaters and a yellow scarf. When I went to pay for the books I saw the cashier could only work with one of her hands and her other hand hung loosely at her side. What do all those people who work there think about welfare?

June 2

Miss A. said all of my grades were good enough for college. She showed me the application forms. Miss A. said there were a lot of scholarships in the country. You just had to apply for them. She said, when the time came, she would help me. Miss A. is a *real* English teacher. She gives me lists of books to read and asks me questions about the books to make sure that I know what I read. This is just between us, after class. I know she is curious about where I live, how I live and if I dared, I would invite her to our room in this building. It is something she should see. But that might frighten her away. She might begin to see me in another way. Maybe the same way my landlady looks at me, with her face full of pity as though I am already dead and somebody forgot to bury my body. I wrote a book report for Miss A. on *The Tale of Two Cities*, which she said was excellent. She is the only teacher who gives me the praise which I think I deserve, who dares to be a teacher. She doesn't want to make my life stand still. I can feel my body growing. I want to feel my mind growing. I want it to grow like the trees I see in Central Park, the trees stretching out, able to support themself, coming to new life each year, set firm, able to live through all the cold winters. Miss A. tries to get the class to believe words are important. She tries to get us to speak in full sentences. She tries to get us to state our thoughts.

It must seem strange to Miss A. that it is so impossible for children born right here on 104th Street not to be able to speak their native language, not to be able to say what they really mean in words. Miss A. tries. But sometimes her face is far away, as though she cannot believe where she is at, facing a roomful of children who would mostly like to tear her to pieces because she threatens their lives with what they don't know and can't seem to learn. This is painful. Some of the class gets up and runs out of the room as though they are going to be attacked by wild dogs. I know knowledge is painful. It hurts me to learn because then I learn how much I don't know. Sometimes I try to shut it out. Sometimes I slam a book shut. Sometimes I tear up a paper I have written for Miss A. Sometimes I want to run out. Sometimes I want to throw books at the blackboard. Sometimes I want to scream at Miss A. and the other teachers, Look at me, don't look at what's in the books, look at me and see the water going over my head and see that I can't scream because the water is filling my mouth. These are the silent screams in all the classes I have. The teachers must *learn* to see the building I live in on West 104th Street. They must *see* the buildings on 103rd Street. They must see what happens on the roofs on 107th Street. They must see that all of the knowledge in the world is not enough to make knowledge important if you don't feel its for you. I thank God for Miss A. who makes me feel a book is worth reading. Momma says, Why are you always reading? I don't answer her. Harriet says, What's in those books? I am afraid that even with the Golden dictionary Edgar will never really know what is in books.

June 3

The investigator came today. I was home with Momma. Edgar was sleeping. Harriet and Charles were on the stoop. I pretended to be reading while the investigator talked to Momma. The investigators don't like the children to be present when they talk. What can they say that we don't know? Why does everyone feel a terrible shame about welfare? I wish Momma could feel a big enough shame to be off of welfare. But how would we live? Momma could work and I could look after Edgar. Or Momma could hire someone to look after Edgar. Some of the women do it. I have two girl friends who make $1 a hour for looking after three babies. Whatever money Momma makes working would be more than we get from welfare. What kind of work could Momma do? I see women working in the dime stores on Broadway and other stores. Some women do housecleaning. They get good money for it and a lot of extra clothes and furniture. Momma finished high school. She could work in an office. Or for the city.

The investigator asked Momma if she had been out looking for an apartment. Momma lied again and said yes. The investigator asked if she found anything. Momma said nobody would rent to her with four children. The investigator said, You have to lie and not say how many children you have. The investigator said, It's hard to put somebody out once they are living in an apartment. The investigator asked Momma if she had heard anything from my father. Momma looked toward me to see if I was listening. I buried my head in the book and didn't look up. Momma said, No, nothing. The investigator said they were after him at the welfare office to locate all the missing fathers on his caseload. The investigator mentioned the name Robert Jones. Is Robert Jones the name of my father or is that a name Momma just gave the welfare people so they would have a name for the record?

I looked in the telephone book to see if there were any Robert Jones. There were some Robert Jones. Would one of them be my father? Did the investigator look in the telephone book? This was the first time in all the years that I heard the name Robert Jones. Momma always shooed me out of the room when the investigator would start to ask questions. Today she didn't.

I don't know why.

The investigator asked Momma, What did Robert Jones do for a living when you knew him?

Momma said, He worked on a truck.

What kind of truck? the investigator asked.

Momma said, A truck that made deliveries.

Did Momma remember the name of the company? Momma said, No. Where was the trucking company? the investigator asked. It's in the record, Momma said. Sometimes you remember things that aren't in the record, the investigator said. He might have social security, the investigator said. He might have veteran payments. He might have income that your daughter could get someday, the investigator said. We don't know until we get hold of him and find out, the investigator said.

That man has nothing, Momma said. He wasn't a man then, Momma said. He was just helping out on a truck. He wasn't more than 18. We just made it a couple of times and then I was pregnant. I never went to him telling him that he gave me a baby. I said it to him once and he looked at me like I was talking to somebody else. He signed a paper but he never made any payments. For two years the welfare people kept deducting his payments from my check without ever making it up. I was always short $10 a check. The investigators would never send me the money. It looked good on your books that he was sending me money. I had to fight you people to get that $10 taken off my budget so that I could get my full check. Nobody has seen that man for 10 years. Not me, not the welfare people, not the courts and not his daughter. Now you come and talk to me about him. *You* find him. You've got his social security number. He's no criminal, he's just a man who doesn't want to be a father. He shouldn't be so hard to find. You just never tried looking. Maybe you want his daughter to go looking for him. You find him. You drag him into court. You make him into a father. You make him give up his salary. You put him in jail if he won't, Momma said. Don't come asking me stupid questions, Momma said. You don't give me enough money for that.

The investigator said, I've got a job to do.

Momma said, You better find out what your job is. I don't think you know.

The investigator got red in the face. He closed his black book.

If I were you, the investigator said, I would move the hell out of this building and fast, living here gives you a big mouth but it doesn't mean anything as long as you live in this filth.

Momma just glared at him. He left.

Are you sleeping? Momma said to me when he left.

June 4

I walked into the Museum of the City of New York. It is directly across the park from 104th Street. There is a room full of old carriages with all of the brass shining, looking newer than any subway or bus I have ever ridden in. There are rooms with polished furniture showing the way families used to live in New York. There are cases full of dolls. Somebody managed to save the old fire engines. I can see nothing worth saving in the world I see except life itself.

June 5

Charles nailed a piece of wood into the wall and it holds the books I bought for Edgar. Momma said the bible I got her was nicer than the one her mother had.

June 6

I walked to the tomb of General Grant and his wife today. They are buried together on Riverside Drive and 122nd Street, which is just a fifteen minute walk from 104th Street. The tomb is quiet. It is nice the way they lay side by side. Not many great men I imagine are buried alongside of their wives. But after seeing what I have seen of the earth I would like to be buried at sea. It must be so quiet at the bottom of the sea. The water is always moving. It would not feel as hard and heavy as the earth over you. I wonder why more people aren't buried at sea. Maybe in time we will be buried at sea. When we have run out of burying land. The tomb of General Grant is supposed to be one of the great sights in America, yet it is only a fifteen minute walk from 104th Street.

June 7

I knew that none of us would be able to sleep when the warm weather began. The heat is terrible in this room. We sleep with the blankets off of us. Our room is on the side of the building and I can hear the garbage bags flying past our window to land in the courtyard. The pile of garbage is building up. It looks like a hill now from the outside. How will the garbage men clear it away when the garbage keeps coming down every day? At night we hear the bottles breaking against the wall. The hot weather is bringing back the rats. They keep scratching where we nailed the tin plates. One night they will break through.

Momma keeps the windows closed. She still hasn't bought the chicken wire. She says she can't open the windows until she nails up the chicken wire because the rats will climb up from the pile of garbage into our room. It would be so easy if Momma would move into a building where there is none of this. The building on Central Park West has an elevator and a doorman and the only trouble they seem to have is from the screams at night from the people in this building that keep them awake and some of them get beaten and their money taken away.

Why won't Momma move? This is the question that I keep asking and I have no one to discuss it with.

I tried to talk with C.M. about it. Her mother has one son with TB, one son with asthma, a daughter with back trouble. They live on the top floor. Their father is in Rockland State Hospital and C.M. tells me he will never come out again. Sometimes they give him pills and he is permitted to come home on a pass. But the last time he had a butcher knife in his coat pocket and he tried to kill C.M.s mother. He cut her very bad on the face and the police dragged him down the stairs. With all the sickness in the family they shouldnt live in one room.

C.M. told me a story and if it is true about Momma then I will be sick to my stomach. C.M. said her mother started to look for a place and then she stopped. She began finding all kinds of excuses of why she couldnt find a new place to live. First it was the landlords who wouldnt rent to a big family. Then welfare wouldnt pay the rent if she did find a place. Or the welfare worker wouldnt get the new rent money in time for her to pay the landlord. Or the new place would be too far. Too far from what? Then it was steps. C.M.s mother couldnt go down the five flights of stairs. Then it was C.M.s mothers own sickness. Then she didn't have any excuses. She just stopped looking and blamed all of her troubles on welfare. The welfare put her into this building, the welfare got her four children she didn't want, the welfare scared away her husband and made him crazy, the welfare put her on the top floor so that she couldnt get out into the street.

June 8

C.M. told me she and a boy are making out. She is trying to get a baby. C.M. says this is the only way she will be able to get away. If she has her own baby she can go to welfare and get her own case and keep her own room. C.M. told me that with her own room and just a baby she can keep a room neat. C.M. said she isn't pregnant yet. She says maybe they are trying to hard. They do it on the roof. C.M. says they are always afraid of being caught or maybe being surprised by a gang of boys. Then the gang might throw her boyfriend off the roof and just keep making out with her over and over again. This has happened on the roof. A.G. in room 407 had 15 boys in her and they kept her on the roof for 3 hours. Her mother took her to St. Lukes for a cleaning.

C.M. told me that there are 5 girls in her class who are pregnant. I only know of one in my class.

Is this what happened to Momma?

June 9

Miss A. showed me some pictures of colleges today. They look like castles in English storybooks.

June 10

Miss A. asked me today to mark some spelling test papers for her. When I was 5 years old Momma used to put up big letters on the wall that she made out of cardboard. The letters would stay on the walls until I could spell the words. Then she would add more letters. I hope she remembers to do the same for Edgar. Most of the test papers I marked were below 50. Miss A. picked words for the test that we should all know, she said. How strange it must seem to her that only three in the class could spell *history*.

June 11

Momma caught me staring at her after dinner. I wonder why we hate to be stared at. It seems we never stand still long enough for any one person to get a good look at us. I was really thinking of Miss A. when I was staring at Momma. Could Miss A. sit down to dinner with us for one night of her life without showing any sign that the room made her sick to her stomach? Could she eat the dinner we had tonight, peanut butter sandwiches and beef noodle soup? Would she come if I invited her? I think what I mean is that I would like to be invited to Miss A.'s house. She must have more than one room to live in. It would take a room this size just to keep all of her books and papers. She needs a desk to read our homework. I heard L. say that Miss A. lived on East 75th Street. I can take the 79th Street crosstown bus and walk past her house. I can look for her name on the mailbox. I can ring her bell. I can say I was just walking past her house, going to the Metropolitan Museum. She would invite me into her room which must be furnished in the shining wood that I see in the magazines in the library, white globes of lamps, white rugs handwoven in Scandinavia. Her books must be on white shelves hanging onto the wall, without any supports showing, graceful and clean. They would look good even in this room on 104th Street. Miss A. would have a big coffee table with a white marble top. She would make fresh coffee in an electric percolator. She would bring out from her kitchen a tray with cakes. Her walls would be white. There would be a Princess telephone on her desk. Her bathroom would have a sliding glass door. There would be a grass green rug on the bathroom floor. The faucets would be shining brass. Thick heavy towels would hang ready to soak up the hot water from the shower. The smells would be like a drugstore at Christmas time. Her bed would be queen size with a headboard to hold more books, another telephone, lamps. Maybe we would just talk over the coffee and cakes, without questions, the way people talk who have known each other for years.

I think I should do it. Take the 79th Street crosstown bus and walk over to Miss A.'s house. I must learn to go to more places. I must make up my mind to travel further than the

A&P. I must go alone on a subway or bus and look at the strange sights of this city. I must walk up Fifth Avenue and look into the windows as though I can have a choice or at least know what choices other people have to make. I must see City Hall which our textbooks say is the most beautiful public building in America. I must go to the top of the Empire State Building and look out on the city that has been my home. I must see the tall buildings on Wall Street and go out into the harbor and feel that there is an ocean all around me. If only the wind would carry the salt air of the Atlantic down to 104th Street. This is an island. I was born on an island. People who are born on islands go out to sea. They seek and explore. *Captain oh captain thy fearful trip is done.* He was right to call him a sailor. We must all go to sea. Miss A. and myself can talk about such things in front of her white marble coffeetable. She had me memorize *Captain oh captain.* And she made me guess that it was Lincoln who was the captain. We are not such great strangers, Miss A. and myself. In class we know how to speak to one another. She always knows how to ask me the question I want to answer, and it is a question that she puts directly to me, and in this way I can tell her I still want to learn. I don't want learning to ever end for me. I wonder what Miss A. is learning from life?

June 12

Mrs. J. had a big fight with her welfare investigator. She was screaming that she would kill him. Mrs. J. lives in room 301. She has six babies in her room. When you walk into her room the babies all look like worms. They sleep in one bunk bed. Three on top, three on the bottom. Mrs. J. has a folding cot for herself. The oldest baby is 7. I sometimes babysit for Mrs. J. She gives me 50 cents. Her room is in a dark corner.

I don't know how she feeds the six babies in the room but she does.

How does the welfare permit her to stay in the room with the six babies? They all look so sick. One of her babies, Ralph, has TB. The investigator said she had to take all of the babies to the chest clinic on 126th Street to see if any of the other babies had TB. Mrs. J. said she wouldn't take them, she said welfare wanted to take her babies away from her, she would be left without her babies if she took them to the TB clinic. The investigator said she had to do it. Mrs. J. said she didn't have to do anything, she wouldnt give up her babies. The investigator said her case could be closed. Mrs. J. said, Nobody would let 6 babies starve, not even welfare. The investigator said the babies wouldnt be taken away, it was just a test. Mrs. J. said he was a lying bastard. The investigator said the babies might all have TB and they could give it to her and the other people since they all used the same toilet. Mrs. J. said, Do you think I care? The investigator said that if she didn't listen to reason, then he would close her case and she could do whatever she wanted to but as long as her case was with welfare they had a legal responsibility to do what was right. Mrs. J. screamed at him, You people are insane if you think having people living in this building is doing what is legally responsible. You son of a bitches put me in here. You gave me this referral. You said it would only be temporary. Well temporary is now two years. If my baby has TB its because of you people. You gave it to him. Now you want to put all my babies in an institution. I won't let you do it. You won't split them up. Right now all they got in this world is each other. If you split them up they are dead to living. I didn't know Mrs. J. could speak in such a way. I guess when people talk about themselves and what is real, they talk differently, and they don't hide behind the words they are saying. Mrs. J. figured out a plan to have her children X-rayed for TB. She is going to take them one at a time. She pays me 50 cents when I stay to watch the others.

June 14

I walked from 104th Street, through Central Park, to where Miss A. lives. It *is* a beautiful building. The brass is polished. The windows are shining clean. The wrought iron railing is painted a rich black. Everybody was busy on the streets near Miss A.'s house. They walked very fast. They stopped taxis. They seemed to be rushing in and out of stores. They seemed to all be going someplace. They carried packages. The traffic never stopped on Madison Avenue. It didn't seem to stop on Miss A.'s street. I watched her building. It looked so safe. Nobody could enter it who didn't belong there.

Then I saw that the buildings didn't look too different from the houses I passed on the West Side streets coming to Miss A.'s house. Only on the West Side the blinds are torn, the windows dirty, the doors broken, and all the radios seem to be playing the same loud song over and over again. Here there was quiet. But the people looked busy. On the West Side the people look as though they can never run again.

June 15

Mrs. C. asked me to sit to watch her children. She said she had to go to court to get a paper signed. This is a warrant saying she will have her husband arrested when she sees him. Momma has to go down to the court to get the same paper.

She puts it in her purse and there it stays. She said if she has Edgar's father arrested he'll come back and kill her. Mrs. C. is a fat woman. She looks 50 but she is only about 35. There is a big scar on her neck. She has five children. One of them is always on the floor when I go into her room.

This time when Mrs. C. went to the court I tried to pick up the baby boy on the floor to see if he could stand. He can't stand. His feet crumble under him. He started to cry. I tried again to see if he could stand. His feet are twisted. Does Mrs. C. know his feet are twisted? I asked her when she came back from court. She said, He is always on the floor. I said, His feet are bad. Did you take him to a clinic? I thought he was a slow walker, Mrs. C. said. He can't walk, I said. Mrs. C. said she would take H. to St. Lukes Hospital.

Didn't Mrs. C.'s investigator notice H. on the floor, didn't he see that he couldn't walk and barely crawl? What are investigators supposed to see? Momma's investigator has never said a word to me. I think there is a law at the welfare building that investigators are not supposed to speak to the children because the children might be ashamed to learn they are receiving welfare or they have no fathers or their mothers are not married. Momma's investigator has never spoken to anyone but Momma. He looks at us as though he is ashamed that we are alive. He doesn't know what to do with us. With Momma he can make speeches. One day I will ask him to explain to me what welfare is and what his job is supposed to be. I know at school the teachers are supposed to teach even if they don't teach. But the investigator seems to be like a policeman yet he doesn't act like a policeman. He writes and writes in his book. Who sees what he writes? Will I ever be able to see Momma's case record? One day I will play a game with Momma and pretend that I am an investigator and as her the questions that she always gives lying answers to, to her investigator.

June 18

School will soon be over. Miss N. my math teacher quit. Miss N. once gave me a 100 on my work. One day she asked me what I wanted to be. I told her I wanted to be a United States Senator. Miss N. stared at me, not knowing how to take what I said. I saw a little bit of fear in her face of the idea that I might be a United States Senator.

June 20

C.M. told me she is pregnant. She said she won't tell her mother anything until she learns that she can get her own welfare check.

June 22

I asked Momma if we could go out today looking for an apartment. I said I would go with her. Momma said she couldn't walk, her feet hurt.

June 23

I asked Momma again today if we could go out looking for an apartment. Momma said we'll find a place when school is over.

June 24

I have a piece of rock that is millions of years old. I hold it in my hand and stare at it. It is a piece of rock I picked up in Inwood Park. Mr. L. our science teacher said some of the rocks in Inwood are the oldest rocks in creation. The piece of rock in my hand may date from the beginning of the world as we know it. We went by the 8th Avenue subway to Inwood Park. The park is at the very northern tip of Manhattan Island. On the way to the park, going up Isham Street we passed rocks that looked as though they belonged on the moon. The rocks are in a little park called Isham. Mr. L. showed us the ruins of an old house that used to stand on top of the hill. The moon looking rocks have no fence around them. They are just out in the open. I saw children from the neighborhood playing on the rocks. The rocks are whiteish looking, ragged, twisting upward, looking like all of the imagined drawings of the moon in our science book. I would put a fence around the rocks and save them. Because sooner or later boys in the neighborhood are going to break the rocks, smash them, just because they are there to be smashed. A beautiful park of rocks will be ruined. Mr. L. told us the rocks looked the way they did because glaciers had crushed them thousands and thousands of years ago. He showed us the rips on the rocks where we could see the path of the glacier.

Going into Inwood Park I saw apartment houses built on hills. The windows looked out into the park. The whole park is their playground. How much cleaner this park looks than Central Park!

We entered the park through a narrow walk. Big trees were on all sides of us. I have never heard such silence. The cries of the birds were sharp and clear. It was almost frightening to be in the midst of such silence. But beautiful. Suddenly there was no more city. We went deeper into the woods. Mr. L. showed us clam shells high on a mound above the water. He said, This is where the Indians used to have their meals. The shells have been untouched since the Indians dropped them there on the mound hundreds of years ago. On one side of us were high hills that went straight up into the air. Mr. L. stopped in front of a steep hill. He pointed up to a cave. He told us that this was the first habitation of human life on Manhattan Island. He said Indians used to live in the cave and in other caves on the sides of the hills. We started up the hill to see the cave. The hill was steep but it felt wonderful climbing up. Mr. L. showed us the smoke covered roof of the cave. He said this was proof that the Indians used the cave. He said Indian pottery had been found in the cave and it was in a museum on 155th Street. We were high up and could look out on a sea of trees. We climbed on the rocks.

Mr. L. showed us another cave we could crawl into. Only this cave had beer cans in it. Why didn't we stop to clear out all of the beer cans?

We went down the hill and came to a sea of water. Beyond the water was a huge rock and a red brick apartment house stood on top of the rock. How do people get to live in such houses? They could see the sun rise and the sun set. Mr. L. took us over to a big boulder that had a brass plaque on it. The brass plaque said that this was the very spot where the Indians sold Manhattan island to the dutch. So history is true. Mr. L. pointed to the fields beyond the rock. He said to the south of us the Indians planted their corn and in one of the fields there had been an Indian burial ground. A cliff rose in front of us. We started up the cliff, going higher and higher until we could see the water below us and houses in the distance. We could only hear the silence. Mr. L. took us off the path and we started climbing down the cliff coming to big rocks. Mr. L. said a glacier had carved out the valley. He showed us an underground pot hole where the water bubbled out. He showed us the ruins of old houses that used to stand in the park. The houses were deep in the forest. Is this really New York City? We went up another ridge. There in front of us was the Hudson River. It was so long. The river flowed toward hills. On the other side of the Hudson River were tall cliffs. Mr. L. said these were the palisades. He said they to were made by the glaciers. He said we were looking out on one of the great sights of the world and I believed him. The palisades seemed to rise straight out of the Hudson River. Upward and upward they rose. Down below the ridge where we stood was a park and the shore of the Hudson. Mr. L. showed us a mound of rocks that had been crossed by the glacier. The glacier had torn ridges across the rocks and left its own signature. I wish I could read the rocks as Mr. L. reads them.

This was the first home of life on Manhattan Island. The caves, the silent forests, the giant trees and the birds. Everywhere we heard birds and saw them swooping from tree to tree. Mr. L. said most of the wild life had fled from the woods but we might still see a pheasant or a jack rabbit. He said we might find arrow heads on the ground where the Indians had dropped them. I saw a big clam shell and picked it up to give to Momma for an ashtray. I picked up the rock I have, this old, old rock that has seen so much history, all of the history of the world.

I didn't want to leave the woods.

The cave I walked into seemed so much nicer than this room. It was cool. It was almost as large as this room. I could live there. Momma and all of us could live there. Charles could go fishing on the rocks on the shore of the Hudson River. Harriet could run through the woods. Edgar could play on the rocks. Momma could sit on the ridge and watch the boats sailing up the Hudson. I could learn the names of all the trees and the birds. I could learn about the Indians who lived in these woods. I could look for traces of their past life. I could dig around the foundations of the old houses and see what I could find of the old history. We could have a boat and sail up the Hudson, or in that beautiful pool of water by the brass plaque where the Indians gave away their home. We could grow food in the woods. There was so much light and air. There was so much of the beautiful sky to see. How does the park exist and this house side by side on the same island only about thirty minutes apart? We could be pioneers again. We should all go out of these buildings and be pioneers. Why are we giving away our lives in this ugly building and in all of the ugly buildings on 104th Street and the streets around us? For whom are we wasting our lives? For this is the way I see it.

The park was beauty and freedom. This is all dying. The streets here. The streets here are like rows and rows of the block buildings that I saw in library books showing pictures of the prison camps of World War two. Rows of wooden buildings and wooden towers with searchlights and machine guns to keep the prisoners in. And almost every prisoner who tried to escape was shot down. I won't be shot down. I will escape. I will run faster than the guards who try to keep me in whoever the guards are. I will run deep into the woods of light and air. How the prisoners in *The Spark of Life* longed to escape. Even the guards wanted to escape. Miss A. said I might like the book. How sad that book was. But how beautiful was the desire to live of the people who were prisoners. How beautiful it was in the park. I thanked Mr. L. for taking us into the park. He was so surprised when I thanked him. He said we would try to go again.

I put the rock on the shelf Charles nailed into the wall. I glued the rock onto a piece of cardboard and I wrote on the cardboard, *From the creation of the world.*

June 25

The police came into the building at 3 A.M. They were banging on the door next to us. They dragged a man out of Mrs. R.'s room. Two welfare investigators were with the police. The man in Mrs. R.'s room couldn't get out. The window was covered up with chicken wire. I heard the man saying, I didn't do anything. I used to see the man come at night into Mrs. R.'s room. He was her real husband. I used to see him bringing in bags of food from the A&P. Mrs. R. has three children. They always had clean clothes on. She tried to keep her room neat even if she couldn't. Mrs. R. was crying in the hallway. She said the welfare would cut off her check. She said she didn't know how she would get money for food. She said the landlord and landlady of the building would throw her out. That would be the best thing that could happen to her.

The welfare people close cases but they open them two days later. They are afraid of letting people scream too loud. You only have to scream to get something. Momma knows this. Screaming will get you everything but an apartment. Momma knows this to.

June 26

Harriet and Charles were doing it when Momma woke up. She saw them and dragged Charles off. She started beating Charles and screaming at him. She picked up a frying pan to beat him over the head but Charles got out of the way of the frying pan. Momma started slapping Harriet. Harriet just let Momma slap her until her hands got tired. Momma sat down on the edge of the bed. She sat that way for awhile and then she made Harriet get into her bed. She put Edgar between me and Charles. She told Charles she would kill him if he put a hand on me. Momma kept the light on. Momma and Edgar slept. The rest of us were awake until morning.

June 27

Miss A. and myself walked to Broadway today from the school. I asked her a question that has been bothering me for a long time. I said to her, In every part of the world, in deserts, mountains, wherever people live, no matter how strange they are or what they do, do they all know they are human, people, do they all see themselves as people? Miss A. said, Yes, everybody alive knows they are alive. Her answer made me feel more alive.

June 28

Charles is gone. Momma waited until 11 o'clock. Then she called the police. The police didn't come till 12:30. Three policemen knocked on our door. One of them swallowed hard when he saw our room. Only two of the policemen could fit into our room. The other one had to stand in the doorway. He kept his hand on his gun. Momma described Charles to the police. They wrote everything down in a black notebook. The policemen asked Momma if she would like to ride around with them for a little while to see if she could spot Charles on the sidewalk. Momma left with the police. I stayed in the room with Harriet and Edgar. Where do you think he went?

Harried asked me. I said I didn't know. Do you know why he left? Harriet said as though she knew. She did know. Charles has been taking money from Momma. Today he took a $5 bill. Harriet said he needed the money to buy some drugs. I said, Where do the pushers expect someone as young as Charles to get $5? You saw that he got it, Harriet said. The pushers know the young ones will steal just as hard as the older ones. I don't believe Charles is on drugs, I said. You don't have to believe it, Harriet said, he is, I knew it before Momma saw the marks on his arms. Then why didn't you tell Momma? I said. I was but she found out. What does Charles say about it? I asked Harriet. He says he'd like to put a knife through the eyes of the ones who got him started on the roof. Is that why he ran away? I asked Harriet, Can't anyone help him? If he doesn't have it bad enough it will go away, Harriet said. But it won't go away if he doesn't have anything else to take its place. Maybe that's the real reason why he ran away, to find something to take the place of the drugs in his system. Harriet and myself talked until Momma came home. Momma was alone. She sat down on the bed.

We didn't find Charles, Momma said. Momma stretched out on the bed. She stared up at the ceiling. The police said he's probably sleeping in a doorway somewhere in the neighborhood. The police said Charles will probably get tired of sleeping in a doorway and come home. The police said a lot of boys run away. The police said they found ten boys sleeping in a burnt-out building on 107th Street. The police asked if Charles belonged to a gang. I didn't know. The police asked me a lot of questions about Charles that I didn't know. (Momma was talking to herself not to us.) The police asked me if Charles had gonohrea or syphilis or whether he was on heroin. What kind of questions are these to ask about a 12 year old boy? The police asked me if Charles ever hustled to the homosexuals in the neighborhood. The police asked me if he had ever been busted. The police asked me if Charles had a job. They saw only two beds in the room and they asked me where Charles slept. One of the policemen asked me why I didn't get the hell out of the building. And all the time I was looking out of the car windows into the sidewalks to see if Charles was there. And if I found him I would bring him back to this room.

June 29

In the morning we all woke up as though none of us had been asleep. We all seemed to be waiting for Charles to knock on the door. Momma gave us each 15 cents and told us to get a Pepsi-Cola. She said she couldn't make breakfast.

June 30

School is over. I passed. Everybody passes. Nobody fails. Some children in my class still can't read or write but they passed to.

July 4

Holiday.

July 5

I was walking on Fifth Avenue today. Not the Fifth Avenue around 115th Street where the drug addicts are as thick as cockroaches. But the Fifth Avenue below 96th Street where the buildings all look like palaces. Just a half a mile separates Fifth Avenue from Central Park West.

I walked past the Metropolitan Museum but I didn't go in. I looked for a minute at Cleopatra's Needle. That stone statue was brought from Egypt. The museum seems to exist to remind people of what they were once capable of doing. I just walked. I looked at the palaces and the doormen who blew whistles like earlier doormen had once blown trumpets. Would I ever be able to hold up my hand and stop a taxi and get in without only having to rush to St. Lukes Hospital for an emergency with Momma? I love to watch people commanding taxi cabs to stop. A horse and a carriage came up Fifth Avenue. A mother with three children sat in the carriage. Momma said this was something she wanted to do for all of the years that she has been alive in New York City but didn't. Can it be that expensive? The woman in the carriage didn't look rich.

On 76th Street I saw somebody who looked familiar. I recognized the walk, the brown hair. Miss A. walks that straight. I walked faster. On 74th Street I was close enough to see her face. It *was* Miss A.

Miss A., I said. She didn't hear me. Miss A., I said a little louder. She still didn't hear me. I walked faster. I caught up to Miss A.

Miss A. smiled when she saw me alongside of her and there was nothing in her eyes and face to say what was I doing on Fifth Avenue.

Would you like to stop somewhere for a Coke or a piece of cake? Miss A. asked me. I said yes.

Let's go in the park, Miss A. said, we're close to the restaurant in the zoo. We walked side by side. Miss A. was wearing a blue skirt and a red jacket. She wore a white blouse.

We went into the park. We stopped to watch the seals eating. We looked at the tigers. We looked at the polar bears. I heard a lion roar. Bright colored birds flew high in a cage. The sun was out. The restaurant looked beautiful in the sunlight. The tables were filled with people who looked like they enjoyed just sitting still and looking at the sun-filled day. We found an empty table on the terrace. Miss A. said, You sit here and hold the table, they're scarce when the sun is out.

Miss A. brought back Cokes and chocolate cake. Now I could see her face. In the sunlight her face looked fresher and cleaner than it does in class. Her eyes are green. Her hair is a deep brown. Her fingernails didn't have polish but they looked clean and shining anyway. She only wore lipstick. A soft red shade. Well, Miss A. said, how do you like Fifth Avenue?

I like the doorways to the buildings, I said, they all look so important.

Imposing, Miss A. said. But so are the rents.

How much would a family pay to live here? I asked Miss A.

It depends, she said, whether the building is rent controlled or not. But rents can go as high as $1,000 a month or more.

I said, That's more than welfare will pay.

Miss A. laughed.

Did you ever live on Fifth Avenue? I asked Miss A.

No, she said.

I sipped on my Coke. Miss A. cut into her chocolate cake.

I don't have to worry about calories, Miss A. said, everybody in my family is slim.

Do you have a big family? I asked Miss A.

If you call three brothers and two sisters big, she said.

Is your father and mother living? I asked.

Yes, Miss A. said. Daddy says he's never going to retire. He said he doesn't like those stories about men who work on railroads who die 18 months after they retire.

Does your father work for a railroad?

No, Miss A. said. Daddy is a lawyer. But sometimes I think he would have preferred to work on a railroad. Daddy likes things that move, that go from place to place. On the weekends he lives on his sailboat. Sailing is a passion for him. He goes out alone and lets the boat drift with the wind. Daddy doesn't believe in winning races.

Is your father rich? I asked Miss A.

Daddy is what you call comfortable middle class. I don't think Daddy has ever thought about money in his lifetime. It just came to him.

What do your brothers and sisters do?

One is a lawyer to, one is an engineer, one is in Washington with the Department of Labor. One of my sisters teaches at Antioch College. The other sister is finishing college.

Do you get together on holidays? I asked Miss A.

Just Thanksgiving and Christmas. Then the house in New Rochelle looks like a Christmas tree. Daddy was lucky in that he bought a big white rambling house that he loves. I think most men suffer with their houses. But I remember

Daddy always going around the house, looking at the paneling on the walls, the ceilings, the banisters, the wooden floors, the big stone fireplace, the porch that had a view of the water. I remember Daddy running his hand over the wood, the walls, Daddy saying that a house is a living thing, if you don't take care of it it falls apart, it goes to ruin. Daddy could feel the house breathing, living. To him the house was alive. Daddy did a lot of work on the house himself. He made a stone wall. He made a stone walk. We have big trees around the house that Daddy planted. I remember when we were all very young Daddy built a treehouse for us in one of the big old oak trees. The treehouse was beautiful. Daddy built a ladder out of branches to go up to the treehouse. The treehouse had a big platform. I would eat there during the summer. It was nice to sit there with a book. It was high off the ground. You were really a part of the tree and the trees around you. The birds weren't afraid to come near you. Daddy taught us all sailing. He built a big barbacue out of old stones. He would do the cooking there when we came back from sailing. Then we would sit on the porch and watch the white sailboats. My room had slanting walls. My bed was by a window. I could see the full moon out of my window. I remember the first time Daddy let me see the moon through his telescope. I stared and stared at the moon hanging in the sky and then I said to Daddy, It's the real moon! Daddy has told that story a thousand times, saying we are always startled by what is *real*.

Is your father old now? I asked Miss A.

I don't think Daddy will ever get old, Miss A. said. He's to involved. Daddy says that men with causes never get old. Daddy still reads. He sometimes says that he wants to die with a book in his hand.

Miss A. finished her chocolate cake. I finished mine.

For a minute we just sat without talking. A breeze was blowing. Miss A. said, This is the kind of breeze Daddy likes for his sailing. Just enough breeze to carry him over the water. Daddy took me out once in his boat far out in the Sound. Beyond us was the ocean. Then the wind died. The air was still. Daddy and myself just sat there in the stillness. Then I remember looking at Daddy and thinking that my life came from him. Out of him my life began. A great part of him was in me. It was then that I saw for the first time how the world is linked from the very beginning of time. That we all went back to a common ancestor. But it will take new worlds in space to convince us of our common link. In that stillness on the water I felt it. Just as this stillness here in the park does it. Do you see the way the people are sitting here? They don't feel they are alone. Not with the trees, the animals, the birds, the visible sky. I wish we had more parks in this city. I wish we could tear down whole blocks of buildings and let more sunlight in. You will be alive in the 21st century, Miss A. said, maybe it will have a meaning that this century can't seem to find. Miss A. said, I've done all the talking. I said, I wish I could say the same things you have been saying.

This is the first time in my life that I have been able to put down the words and places that came to me as real as life in my sleep without forgetting every single word on getting out of bed.

July 7

Charles hasn't come home yet. Momma calls the police and they tell her nothing. Harriet and myself have been out on the street looking for Charles. We walked from 110th Street and Broadway to 72nd Street. We thought Charles would be looking in all of the store windows on Broadway. Harriet and myself realized that Charles has no friends. We couldn't think of a single boy we could go and see who might know something about Charles. Maybe like P.K. he was ashamed to bring friends to the room on 104th Street. Where does he sleep at night? The police said in hallways. Maybe that is the place to look. But where does Charles wash? Where does he eat? Who does he talk to? Has he talked to anyone since he ran away? What does he do all day long? Momma called her two cousins in the city. They said Charles didn't call them.

What if Charles is dead? But if he was dead his body would be resting someplace. Dead bodies don't remain out in the open. Only the living dead. This is what the investigator told Momma, you'll be one of the living dead if you don't move. Maybe Charles ran away not to be dead. But he was already dead in the room. He didn't watch TV. He never opened a book. He never looked at a comic book. He just stayed in bed or went up to the roof. There on the roof he got something that made him a little happy. I can't remember now what Charles talked about.

It frightens me that I can't remember. Did he want to be a doctor, a fireman, a businessman, or what, an athletic making $10,000 a week? Miss A. said black athletics make more money than anybody else who is black. I know Charles didn't like welfare. Momma bought him a new pair of shoes on 102nd Street. He wore the shoes to school. During the lunch period the boys got around him and started yelling, Welfare shoes, welfare shoes! What can Momma do? The investigator tells Momma to go to work. Momma says, Who will look after Edgar? The investigator says, I don't know.

Momma doesn't have to work as long as the government sends us checks. Miss A. said the money is for us to grow up, me,

Harriet, Charles and Edgar. Did the government mean it to be like this? With Momma in bed half of the time cursing Charles and the other half of the time crying.

It is now 8 days since Charles is gone. He must be dead or so hungry that he can't move or so mad that he never wants to come back to 104th Street.

July 9

For two days now Momma has been crying. She says she is sure that Charles is dead. The police have nothing to tell her. Nobody on 104th Street has seen Charles. The landlord and landlady keep asking Momma about Charles. Momma doesn't answer them. A letter came in the mail today saying that Charles could go to camp for two weeks. There is supposed to be a letter for me and Harriet. Then Momma will have to go see her investigator and fight to get camp clothes for us. The camp sends a long list of what we need. A flashlight, a duffle bag, tennis shoes, bathing suit, shorts. Charles will miss camp.

Momma calls the place where they keep dead bodies every day. Momma talked to three gang leaders on Columbus Avenue. They told her Charles didn't belong to any gangs. Momma says, How can a 12 year old boy be on the streets this long?

July 10

The police found Charles. Two policemen in a squad car saw a boy going into a grocery store. He came out carrying a bag. The police saw there were three large bottles of beer in the bag. Children aren't supposed to be able to buy beer. They asked Charles to take him to the person he was buying the beer for. It was a room on West 84th Street. Charles took them to the 3rd floor. In the room was a white man. The police said he was a homosexual. He picked up Charles and took him to his room. He fed Charles and gave him fifty cents a day. Charles slept in the same bed with him. They did things that Momma screamed about. She screamed and screamed when the police told her the whole story. Charles stood very cold when Momma screamed. He stood cold and stiff. I have the feeling he will never be part of our family again. His eyes don't seem to blink. He barely noticed me and Harriet. I heard one of the policemen say, He's going to go the route now. The police said Charles would have to appear in court, get a physical examination and the court would have to decide what to do with him—if they could, I could hear one policeman whisper. The police arrested the white man.

July 11

I said to Momma tonight, If we move into a nicer house, the judge might let Charles come back with us.

July 15

Momma went to court today. We stayed at home to watch Edgar. Momma came home with Charles. He looks so big and old now. He looked bigger than the room. I don't see how he'll fit in the bed with us. Momma only said the judge didn't have any place to send Charles now. Charles is on probation. That means he has to do what the court tells him to do. The court told him to stay out of trouble, and to obey Momma. This is what Momma repeated to Charles. Charles just listened.

July 17

Momma told Charles to sleep with Edgar. Momma is in our bed. It is hot. We have no fan. The air doesn't move. Momma got out of bed to put some cold water on her face. Charles got up and said Edgar wet the bed. Momma yelled at Charles to go to sleep. Charles sat in the chair. He said, I can't sleep in piss. Momma got out of bed and hit Charles. Charles lifted his hand to hit Momma then he put his hand down. Momma said, You could sleep with that white one. Charles said, He didn't piss in bed. Momma said, He did worse. Charles didn't answer. Edgar woke up crying. We heard fire sirens. I hoped our building was on fire and that it would burn to the ground. Then welfare would give us new furniture, new clothes, new shoes, new dishes, new pots, new pans, new everything. But the fire was across the street. I could smell the smoke. The smoke mixed with the heat was terrible. Momma said she was going outside to sit on the stoop and get some air. I asked Momma if I could see the fire. Momma said we should all stay in the room.

When Momma left I asked Charles why he ran away. Charles didn't answer me. But Charles reached in his pocket and took out a $10 bill. He said the white man gave it to him. Charles then told us about the boys he saw on 84th Street and the other blocks around there and he said some of them made up to $150 a week. He said the boys sat in the park on 72nd Street or on the benches on Broadway. He said none of them would take a regular job because they could make a $100 even if they couldn't read or write. Harriet said, What do you have to do to make so much money? Charles said, You know what. Harriet said, Did you make a $100? Charles said he was just learning. Harriet said, Will you go back there? Charles said,

What can keep me away? I said, What if the court sends you away? Charles said, Everyplace is filled up, for the first time they'll leave me stay, maybe the next time they'll send me away. Charles talks about himself like he is talking about somebody else. How did he get this way? What did he learn? I wish he would talk more. He seems to be hiding so many mysteries.

Harriet said to Charles, Will you run away again? Charles said, I will go away. It is hard to believe Charles is only 12. He seems so wise yet he can't read a 3rd grade book. He can't spell words. He doesn't do better than 1st grade math. I did all his homework when he got homework. I tried to tell Charles what was right in math and spelling. He said that was for somebody else.

But Charles knows the verses to over 50 rock and roll songs. How could he learn them all if he doesn't know how to spell *elephant?*

I watched Charles sitting on the chair. He was studying the room. He is slipping away. He no longer sat in the room like he used to, like this was the place where he lived. Those days are gone. Charles is slipping away into the street. The street is the place where the grown up men live who have no other place to live. Edgar's father lives in the street. Momma calls him a hustler. He has no job. He hustles for money. I don't exactly know what this means. But I see the men hanging around the stoops all day while some of the other men go off to work. The police don't seem to bother them. If this is the kind of man Charles is going to be then he will never be a man.

It seems as if there is no one in the world to stop Charles from slipping away into what he is doing now.

Momma came up from the fire and said Mrs. A.R.s apartment burned out across the street and one of the babies may die of smoke poisoning. Mrs. A.R. has 5 babies. Now she may have 4 babies.

Maybe our room will burn next but I don't want Edgar to die of smoke poisoning. I try to talk to Edgar because Momma almost never says a word to him. Momma tells me to stop making so much noise when I talk to Edgar. But I know Edgar likes it when I talk to him or read him stories.

We all fell asleep because when we woke up it was morning. Momma woke up and cried out, Where's Charles? I said he went to the bathroom. Charles came back and said, The toilet is busted again.

Momma said, I'm going to call my investigator to see if he found a place for us yet.

Momma won't listen to the investigator when he tells her that she has to find her own place.

July 18

We have been living here 6 months. Momma said we would only be living here 6 days when we moved in.

August 6

I went to camp and came back to this room.

August 7

I do not believe the camp exists. It is 35 miles from New York City but it could be on the moon. There is so much open land away from the city. Who do all of the trees belong to? Do I have a claim on them? The minute we left New York City on the bus across the George Washington Bridge the trees and the open land came to life. I would rather live in a tent on open land than sleep in this room. At camp I shared a bunkhouse with three other girls. One of them was sent home the second day. She was caught stealing from the other girls. I never got tired of looking at the sky. The stars look exactly the way they are described in books. The stars were so bright, so near. In camp the stars look personal, real. I took swimming lessons in the lake. The water was cool and clean. I couldn't get enough of the swimming period even if I can't swim far or deep. I read the hours I had free time. I finished *Gullivers Travels* and Homer's *Oddessy*. The only time in my life when I slept alone in a bed was in camp. My greatest pleasure was sleeping alone and touching the clean water. My counsellor used to say I could sleep enough at home. How can there be so much open land and so much dirt here? Who decides who lives where? I made an enamel pin for Momma. She looked at it as though she didn't believe it could be made by human hands. So much can be done with human hands.

The bunkhouse I lived in at camp was made out of logs, one log placed on top of another log until you had a house. Momma, Edgar, Harriet, Charles and myself could easily live in a bunkhouse made out of logs. It must cost less to build than a years rent for this room. When I came back to 104th Street this building looked as strange as the trees and the open land when I got off the bus in camp and put my feet on the grass. We must find a place to live where we always don't feel like strangers. The landlady asked me if I had a good time in camp. There is a tree growing in the back of this building but it looks abandoned, like something left over from the past.

The investigator sent Momma enough money to buy me a pair of sneakers, a bathing suit, a flashlight, two changes of underwear, a heavy sweater and a canvas bag for carrying my things. My flashlight was stolen. Did they know in camp I was getting welfare? If they did, how could they send us to camp for only two weeks and keep us fifty other weeks in this building?

August 8

Harriet and Momma are having big fights. Harriet is staying out late. Momma says she must be in by 9 o'clock. Harriet says she wont be in until 11 o'clock. Momma slapped Harriet in the mouth. She asked Harriet where she can stay until 11 o'clock without getting her pants taken down. Harriet yelled at Momma, You did it often enough. Momma smashed Harriet after that.

August 10

Momma has a new investigator. A girl. She came today and left Momma shaking. The new investigator is a black girl. She wouldn't sit down on a chair. She stood all the time. She watched the cockroaches crawl over a loaf of Wonder Bread. She made a face like she was going to vomit. Momma said, You put me in here, your housing advisor said this place would be all right temporarily. The investigator said, I didn't put you in here. She said each word separately. She kept asking Momma about Edgar's father. Then she asked about my father, Harriet's father and Charles' father. Momma said, Its all in the case record. The black girl investigator said, I don't care what's in the record, I want to hear it from you. Momma said, I'm not going to tell these stories all over again, not for you or anybody else from that office. The black girl investigator said, Maybe that's all they are, stories, stories. Don't you want these children to know who their fathers are? Momma said, Watch your mouth. The black girl investigator said, What will you do? Momma said, Stop it for you. The black girl said, Where does the father of Edgar live?

Momma said, I don't know.

The black girl said, Where does the father of Charles live?

Momma said, He's dead, he got killed in a fight on 126th Street and 8th Avenue.

Do you have proof of that, the black girl asked.

I saw him cut up on the sidewalk, Momma said. Two men killed him.

Where's the father of Harriet, the black girl asked.

I haven't seen him in 13 years, Momma said.

Why not, the investigator asked.

I met him at a party on 114th Street. We were together one night. I didn't know his name. Nobody at the party knew his name. I never saw him around again. Somebody said he drove a truck between here and Georgia. But nobody knew his name to prove it. He never told me his name.

What about her? the black girl investigator asked, and she pointed to me. She's the oldest and she was the first.

I pretended I wasn't listening. I waited for Momma to speak as though I was falling and only her voice would hold me up.

You remember the first one, the black girl investigator said.

Momma said to her, Do you?

The black investigator closed her notebook.

Momma wasn't going to speak. I felt my legs were like water.

The black girl investigator opened her notebook again. Let's get it all for the record, she said.

Between Momma and me there was something like a wall of water. We could see each other through the wall of water but we couldn't get past it. The waves kept pushing us back. I waited for Momma to speak.

Momma said, His name was Joseph. He wanted to be a lawyer. But the police busted him when he was 16 for doing nothing except standing on a corner at 123rd Street. It was a hard bust. Joseph got up in front of a crazy judge who had to put everybody away. There were teachers, principals, everybody saying in court that it wouldn't serve any purpose to bust him further. But the crazy judge wouldn't listen. He said the law had to be learned. One of the teachers said a court conviction would ruin Joseph's chance of getting a college degree. The crazy judge said, He isn't going to get a college degree. The judge was a meat chopper. Two weeks before all this happened Joseph and myself made out. Then I never saw him again. We moved six weeks later. I had to have a clinic doctor tell me I was pregnant who saw me for stomach pains. When my mother heard I was pregnant she went crazy. She made me shut up and hide it from everybody till I graduated. I was fat from eating too much, I told everybody. Momma tried to find Joseph. Nobody could find him, not my mother or the welfare people. Momma was on welfare then but respectable welfare. She didn't want anybody to know that to. Now you find him, Momma said.

So you're second generation welfare? the black girl investigator said.

Momma said, Your generation time won't come but you don't know it.

August 11

I know my fathers name was Joseph.

August 14

I saw five well dressed white men in the front of the building today. They were talking to the landlady and the landlord. The landlady said to the five men, If you want to look, look, but remember we don't live in the rooms, we don't make the mess, we don't use the toilet, we don't break them, we repair them, we don't throw our garbage out of the window, we don't smash the locks, we buy new locks, we don't put the garbage in the hallways, we don't smash the bottles, we don't take dope, we have nice tenants, they are quiet and they look for bigger apartments but some of the others are dogs. The five men listened and then they went into the building. I walked behind. Maybe they would close up the building and welfare would have to move all of us. On the first floor, one of the men knocked on room 108 where Mrs. S. lived. She was an old lady of 80 and her bed always smelled. She never left her room. She used a baby's pot for a toilet. She gave one of the drunken men 10 cents to empty the pot everytime it was full. The man in the blue suit knocked on the door. When he opened the door he started vomitting. I heard the landlady say, She's an old woman, it is not my fault that she is old.

The man who vomitted ran toward the street. He vomitted again on the sidewalk. When he finished he got into a car and drove away. The other men stood around. One said, This is a job for the Building Department. Another man agreed. They left the building. I heard the landlady say they were from a reform democratic club. The dogs, she added. The landlady likes this to be her world. She doesn't like intruders. She doesn't like investigators she doesn't know. She sits all day behind the chicken wire. When she saw me looking she tried to give me a white blouse that was three sizes to big.

The landlord looked worried. He always worries. He is afraid that one of the men in the building will kill him. He has a weak heart. Why does he sit here? I can see he hates this building. Maybe the welfare people forced him to take in all the families, all the babies.

On the 2nd floor in room 205, Miss G. has a daughter I used to say hello to. The daughters name is L. L. just had a baby. She moved into a room next to her mother. How is it possible? L. told me that her investigator said it would be all right. The five reform democratic men will never see L.

August 18

In my calendar at school it says the first white child in America was born on this day. Do they know when the first black child was born? A.L. on the 4th floor just had a baby. She is 15. A.L.'s mother has four other babies. The same man who made A.L.'s baby, made her mothers four babies. I see the man in the hallways. He is very tall. He works as a roofers helper. Most of the time he is drunk. I see a big knife sticking out of his pocket. He looks like such a big man to give A.L. a baby. A.L. says she won't stay in the room with her mother. Now A.L. wants her own welfare case. I see now that every girl I know in this building over the age of 13 has a baby or is getting a baby. Who will be first, me or Harriet?

August 19

Today I saw Charles sleeping and he looked like a little boy.

August 20

Miss D.B. from the 3rd floor stopped me today. She looks about Momma's age. She is one of the few women who wears a freshly ironed dress. Miss D.B. said to me, I always see you carrying books. Do you like to read? I said I did. Miss D.B. said to me that her 11 year old boy R. can't read. She said she tried to make him learn how to read. She said she pointed to words in the baby books that she buys and she tries to get him to learn simple words like *boy*, *cat*, *house*, *summer*, *winter*, *play*. But none of the words mean anything to him, she said. Do you think you could help him with reading? I would pay you, she said. The school, she said, hasn't taught him. Can he read any words? I asked Miss D.B. She said, Not in a sentence. I find myself screaming at him, she said to me, and that must make it worse for him but I can't stop from screaming, do you know what I mean? Can you try with a couple of lessons? she asked me. I said I would.

August 21

How will I teach R. to read? I can't remember how I learned to read in school. It seemed to happen, the way I don't remember learning how to walk.

I told Momma what Miss D.B. asked me to do. Momma said it made sense.

August 22

Tonight I sat with R. He is shorter than Charles. He smiles with almost every word that he says, only it isn't exactly a smile. We didn't do much tonight. I didn't know what to do. I brought a book with me that I read to Edgar all of the time. Its a story about a train. When I finished reading the story to R. I asked him to tell me about the story.

What color was the engine? I asked him.

Red, he said.

How many cars did the red engine pull? I asked him.

Five, he said.

What happened to the red engine?

It got turned around on the wrong switch, R. said.

Where was the red engine going? I asked R.

To Philadelphia, he said.

To do what, I asked.

To bring people to see the sights, he said.

Do red engines really talk? I asked R.

No, he said, but they do in stories.

Miss D.B. paid me 75 cents.

August 23

I go to see R. two nights a week.

Tonight I asked R. to write his name. He wrote his name slowly almost as if he was tracing the letters.

Now read your name to me, I said.

My name? he said.

Read your name, I said.

I know my name, he said.

Read your name, I said.

Why, he said.

Because it is your name, I said.

What's so important about my name? R. said. I know my name.

Can you read your name? I asked R.

If I know my name, then I don't have to read my name, R. said.

But if you don't know the name of something, then you have to read it, I said to R.

R. read his name slowly, the way he wrote his name, as though the words were to be read so that they would hang up visible like clothes on a clothes line.

August 24

I gave R. a book tonight to keep. I asked him to write his name in the book, the day of the week, the month, the year.

R. asked me tonight if most stories were make-believe. I told him most stories were true.

R. said tonight he only wanted to read stories that were true.

August 25

I want to ask Miss D.B. why she stays in this house. I think R. would read without me if he had his own bed. He sleeps with his mother. R. told me when his baby brother is old enough to be out of the crib then they will have a bed for the two of them.

August 26

R. knows more words than he has ever let anyone know that he knows.

August 28

Miss D.B. moved. Momma said she came to say goodbye to me but she couldn't wait. She had to meet the super in the building on 82nd Street and she was afraid that she would lose the apartment if she was late. Momma said Miss D.B. said to let me know that R. read the street sign where the new house is.

I bought some plastic flowers with some of the money I made from Miss D.B. Nothing in this room or house can ever destroy the flowers. The roses will always be roses. The lilacs will always be lilacs. Momma says they look real. They look so bright on the table. In the morning when I woke up and saw them on the table they looked plastic to me.

August 29

Momma had to go to court with Charles. Charles is on probation. The judge said Charles must be enrolled in school in September.

August 30

They broke a lot of windows in my school building. I walked past it today.

Momma stopped to listen to a speaker on the sidewalk when we were coming home from the A&P. The speaker held a small American flag in his hand. About 20 people were listening to him, including Mr. L.N. from 104th Street. The speaker said black people didn't know they were black. You all want to be white, he screamed as though the crowd was arguing with him. Awake and sing, the bible says, awake and sing, awake and be black, he shouted. Learn a new song. Awake and be black. The speaker was about 35. He was dressed neat. He spoke in a low powerful voice. Did he make speeches all day? What kind of work did he do to pay his bills? Did he have children, a wife? Did black people believe they weren't black? The speaker seemed to look at me. He was. He pointed a finger at me and said, The black people have ten million prophets, ten million black children are prophets, they will take us out of the wilderness of our minds that are in bondage. Momma said, Let's go. The packages were getting heavy. The investigator once sent Momma money for a shopping cart but the cart was stolen when she left it in the hallway for a minute. The speaker repeated, Wilderness of the mind. We turned toward the wilderness of West 104th Street. I never think about being *black*. I am more concerned about the *me* in me, that part of *me* that I can feel telling me there is a *me*.

August 31

Momma was crying this morning. She sat at the table crying and hitting her hands on the table. Harriet asked Momma why she was crying. Momma didn't look at Harriet. Momma kept on crying. Her face looked so stiff, her skin looked so pulled, as though it would break apart. I asked Momma if I could get her anything from the drugstore. If I should call for a welfare doctor. They come almost immediately when you call them. The ambulances come fast to. Momma didn't listen to me. She cried at the table, hitting her hands. Edgar was crying but she didn't go to pick him up. I picked up Edgar. He was wet. I diapered Edgar. Momma didn't say not to put a diaper on Edgar like she usually does. We asked Momma if anything hurt her. Momma didn't answer us. Momma went downstairs to make a telephone call in the landlords office. She came up still crying. She looked around the room as though she was going to scream.

The heat was terrible. We were all sweating. I touched Mommas arm. It was cold. We asked again if we should call for a doctor or an ambulance. Momma said no. Then she sat at the table just staring ahead of her. She sat like that until it was time to give Edgar lunch. I made cornflakes for Edgar. I couldn't eat. I didn't want to eat. Harriet asked Momma if she should go down and get a Pepsi-Cola for her. Momma didn't answer. I didn't dare leave the room. I just sat there looking at Momma. We all sat in the room except Charles. He was on the stoop. Momma said she couldn't make dinner. She gave Harriet a dollar to buy some liverwurst and a Wonder Bread. Harriet made the sandwiches. I didn't eat my liverwurst. Charles ate. He said to Momma, What's wrong? Momma didn't answer. Momma went into the toilet about seven o clock. She stayed there a long time, about 30 minutes. She came and stetched out in her bed. She lay there a little while then she began to moan. The sheet was covered with blood. I ran downstairs with a dime and called for an ambulance. I ran back upstairs. Momma was still bleeding. Mrs. G.

and Mrs. K. from the next rooms came in. They saw the blood and where it was coming from. They seemed to know what Momma did. The ambulance men came in the room with two policemen. They looked at Momma and said she had to go to the emergency room. I heard the word *abortion*. The two policemen looked at Edgar, Harriet, Charles and me and said, What about them? The ambulance men took Momma down the stairs. The two policemen took us in their squad car to the Children's Center.

September 1

Once before Momma was sick and we had to be away. That time we were all separated. I stayed in a building with nuns who kept calling me little girl. Now we were together. But in different rooms. I went into a room with a lot of beds. The beds were pushed together. I didn't fall asleep but when I woke up it was morning. It looked like school. In some of the beds I saw two girls sleeping. The paint on the walls was cracked. The floor looked broken. We went past a room where all the cribs were pushed together so that you couldn't get past the cribs. I thought Edgar was in that room. But I didn't see him. We washed. I ate something. Everyplace the rooms were filled with children. All I can say about the Childrens Center is that no child should be there.

September 3

Momma came for us. She looked rested after being in the hospital. We walked through the park to 104th Street. There is a direct path. Halfway through the park we sat down on the grass to rest. For a minute or two we looked like a family. At least that is what a stranger would have thought. When we came out of the park we could see all of the buildings on Central Park West stretching as far as we could see. The buildings right next to us were bad. The one next to the big building was rotten. Momma went there to look at a two room apartment. Momma said she would be afraid to sleep there at night. The building was filled with drunken men who stared at you and with women who seemed to be always screaming. It was a dirtier building than ours on 104th Street if that is possible. In our building some of the people seem to want to get out. But in that building on Central Park West the people seemed to want to stay there for the rest of their life. They gave up what they had to give up, which I guess is life.

Momma tried to clean up our room a little. That was the first thing I noticed when we walked in. The garbage was taken out. There were no dishes in the sink. The two beds were made with fresh sheets drawn tight. Two of our dresses were ironed and hanging from a nail on the wall. The bundle of clothes was out of the room, probably at the laundermat. We sat down on the bed, Harriet and me. Momma placed Edgar on the floor. How do we start living again in a room like this after being away for three days? I didn't know what to do first. I wanted to close my eyes and hope that we were just visiting and that in an hour we would be gone. But in an hour we were still in the room. I began to see the cockroaches come out of the walls. Momma had sprayed but the spray was over.

Momma said to me, Why are you just sitting on the bed?

I said I was tired. Momma is too easily satisfied.

Charles came up with five cans of Pepsi-Cola. I drank mine before it became hot. The heat in the room was terrible. My arms and my back was wet. Edgar started to cry.

Momma looked cool. Maybe it was because her new baby was dead. I heard she made herself bleed in the toilet and that killed the baby. Momma could have died from blood poisoning. Harriet told me that if she gets a baby she won't kill it. Harriet told me that she made out with R.L. who lives on 108th Street. They did it once in his house when nobody was home. Once on the roof. Once again in his house. Harriet said that was the best time, because his mother had to be in court and R.L. told her that they had at least five hours. Harriet said she and R.L. were naked in bed. She said it was like being married. She said R.L. did it to her 6 times and each time she hoped it meant a baby. She said she and R.L. figured out that they could live on a welfare check if he could get some money on the side and not tell welfare. R.L. is 16. He is supposed to graduate in a year. But Harriet says he may quit. Harriet like Charles looks different now. Like Charles she is cold toward Momma. But she is still afraid of Momma and doesn't say much. It is just in the way Harriet acts in the room, as though her days are numbered and she will soon be gone. Charles will go any day now. That is certain. I don't know how he will live away from the house but he will find a way. What about me? Will I stay here like Momma, with Momma? Maybe Momma will find an apartment before any of this happens. Harriet should not have a baby. She is only 13. I wish I could work out a plan to make Momma look for an apartment.

I dozed off and woke up sweating all over my body. The heat was worse. The air didn't move. Momma was cooking, boiling frankfurters with sauerkraut. The smell was terrible. We seem to live on frankfurters. A teacher of mine said frankfurters had a lot of protein. So does steak, a boy in the class said to her.

Momma started using paper plates. She said this way the dishes don't pile up in the sink. She said the welfare should put paper plates on the budget, because in these buildings you never knew when the hot water would come out. Momma asked us how we liked the Childrens Center. Harriet said it was terrible but she took two showers. Momma said she would like to move into a building with showers that work. She said most of the junkies rip off the shower heads to sell them.

Charles doesn't say a word. He went down for more Pepsi-Cola.

Momma said hospitals are the cleanest places in the world. Maybe Momma is making up her mind to move.

I went to the toilet but the door was locked. I heard some voices from the toilet. It was C.L. She was saying, Don't you have to wash the needle? I heard A.D. say, It's all sterilized. Then I heard A.D. yelling, Why doesn't this door open? He almost broke down the door coming out. He ran past me. I saw C.L. on the toilet floor. She was laying on her back. I screamed for Momma. People started coming out of their rooms. Momma rushed upstairs. So did the landlord. He looked sick when he saw C.L. on the toilet floor. She was 12. C.L.s mother wasn't home. Nobody knew what to do with C.L. except to call an ambulance. The ambulance drivers said C.L. was sick, from a overdose of drugs.

The police arrested A.D. He was screaming when they took him down the stairs.

Momma bought a folding bed. She slept on the folding bed which took up the center of the space in the middle of the room. Charles slept with Edgar. Harriet and myself slept together.

Harriet asked me to feel her stomach to see if I could feel anything.

September 7

The first day of school is over. I have Miss A. again for English. My day of luck.

September 9

Miss A. started crying in class. She cried out to the class, I want to help you people. A boy yelled back at her, F you.

September 11

My science teacher told the class, I will throw out any student who makes noise. I will throw out everyone if I have to teach to only one student. Is that clear? A boy in the back row yelled out, You go first. The science teacher got up from his desk to go down the aisle when five boys got out of their seats to stand in front of him. The science teacher went back to his desk. If you want to be dumb and not learn its all right with me, he said and he opened a book and didn't look at us. The next day he didn't show up for class. Did he make up his mind beforehand that we were not worth teaching? The class wasn't making any noise. The new teachers will vanish.

Why does Miss A. stay? The new teachers always come into the classroom as if they are in the wrong classroom. The new teachers seem so frightened as though they don't know how to teach us. Is it because most of us are on welfare or most of us live in projects or most of us are black or Puerto Rican or what? Most of the teachers seem to think they are wasting their knowledge on us. They are like the landlord and landlady on West 104th Street, they think they will waste their money by keeping the building on 104th Street clean.

I know a good teacher when we have one. Miss A. She is not afraid. She is not afraid to give up the knowledge she has. The knowledge she has flows from her, you can feel it coming into your own mind and body. It is exciting. It is like feeling you have a real family. Like Momma is when she talks to us about things that she did when she was a little girl, just talking, with something like a smile on her face, only it is more, it lasts longer than a smile, it even makes it possible to sleep at night in the room.

September 15

C.L.s mother didn't have enough money to pay for the funeral for C.L. Momma gave $5. I heard the landlady and landlord gave $20. C.L.s mother collected about $150. That still wasn't enough. The father of C.L. came around. We heard he gave $50.

Welfare allows you to keep some money for burial but if you don't have the money you can't keep it. C.L.s mother was able to make a deposit otherwise the funeral people would have never buried her. There is a place called Potters Field. That is where they put you in a sack in a grave with no name and the grave is a ditch, when you have no money. But welfare should have enough money to bury children. Momma pays on a policy and the policy has enough money to bury us. Momma said she wouldn't go around to neighbors and strangers for money. But C.L.s mother had to, she had no policy. You need to know so much to live in this world.

September 23

The landlord offered Momma a slightly larger room on the top floor at $22.75 a week. Momma said she didn't want to climb five flights. The landlord told Momma that he had two houses in the Bronx where vacancies sometimes came up. Momma asked him about the house across the street. He said welfare would only pay $30 a week if there were 5 children in the family. The landlord said he didn't make the welfare rules. Momma said she would just move in if a vacancy came up and let her investigator get the rent straight.

September 25

A new investigator came today. This a white man about 40. He only stayed about two minutes. He asked to see Momma's rent receipt. He wrote it down in his black book. Then he was gone.

September 28

Charles is gone. He didn't come for supper. He didn't come after 11 o'clock. He didn't come back at all. Momma called the police at 12 o'clock. The police came in a squad car at 1 o'clock. Momma rode with the police until 2:30. She came back and stretched out on the bed. Momma said they went to 84th Street but the white man had moved away. Momma said Charles must have a plan. What kind of a plan can a 12 year old boy have for running away? Momma didn't seem as angry this time. Where Charles was sleeping and how he was sleeping didn't seem to bother her. I wasn't surprised that Charles had run away. I was just surprised at how he was going to live.

September 29

Charles called Momma to say that he was alive. He wouldn't tell Momma anything else.

September 30

A truant officer came to see Momma today. They call them attendance officers now. The attendance officer was a fat man about 50. He had gray hair. He kept looking around the room as though he wouldn't be able to get out. He told Momma that Harriet had missed three days of school in a row. He wanted to know if she had been at home or sick. Momma said she didn't know Harriet had missed school. She said she thought Harriet was at school. The attendance officer said he had to have a reason why Harriet was absent or he might have to make a referral to court. He said Momma could be charged with neglect. Momma told him to get out. She said she was tired of having strangers coming into her house making threats. Momma said she was going to make some threats of her own. She didn't say what they would be but she seemed to frighten the fat man. He said the court is only used if nothing else works.

Momma said, You come back here in three days and I'll tell you why my daughter stayed out of school three days in a row. The fat attendance officer said that would be all right because he had a week before he filed a report. Momma said, What do you do with all the reports? But he didn't listen.

Momma began by slapping Harriet. She hit Harriet twice across the mouth. But Harriet didn't cry. Momma then got out the strap she has kept as long as I can remember. Momma hit Harriet twice across the shoulders with the strap. Harriet still didn't cry. Momma sat down on the bed with the strap in her hand. I didn't cry when I was a girl either, Momma said, I never cried, even when I got hit more than you, I could hit you all day and you wouldn't cry, Momma said.

Harriet didn't speak. Harriet was keeping her face cold. Maybe she was already pregnant and she was going to tell it to Momma like dropping a boulder from Central Park on her head.

Momma said to Harriet again, Why did you stay out of school for three days? Where did you go?

It is funny that Harriet didn't lie. She could have said she went to the movies or she hated her teachers or she went down to 34th Street to windowshop. There were a hundred lies she could have told. But she kept silent. Maybe the truth was the one thing that made her feel important.

Momma said to Harriet, Do you know that that fat white man who was here can take you to court and put you into an institution like a jail where you have no freedom and where each girl is half crazy and they fight and scream all day, is that what you want?

Harriet said no.

Momma said, Then make up a good lie for that fat man.

Harriet said, I went to the movies three days in a row.

With who, Momma asked.

Two other girls.

Where did you get the money? Momma asked.

The girls had the money, Harriet said.

Where did they get the money? Momma asked.

They said they stole it, Harriet said.

Why did you go to the movies? Momma asked.

Because school already stinks, Harriet said. The teachers yell before you do anything and when you do something they get scared. One teacher was knifed in the lunchroom and that makes them all nervous like hungry cats. One mother from 109th Street came to the principal and said her children were dying because they weren't learning anything. I was sitting in the principals office. The woman got up very close to the principal pressing her body against him and she said, The Lord gave you a trust to teach these children and before God you will do it and not have these teachers yelling all day at these children instead of teaching them what they should know, because if they don't learn here they will never learn, it will be all over for them. I heard the principal say under his breath when she left, Black son of a bitch.

Momma said, It wasn't like that when I went to school.

Harriet said to Momma, You should come to school one day Momma and just walk around. You see some of the kids running up and down the halls like they're crazy. In my class at least five kids sleep all the time because they don't sleep at night. The teachers are just as crazy as the kids. Harriet still wasn't telling Momma why she stayed out of school for 3 days. The truth is R.L., Harriet's boyfriend's mother, was in the Womens House of Detention for 3 days and Harriet was in his bed for 3 days.

October 2

The attendance officer accepted the story about the movies. He said movies can be educational too. He was in a hurry to get out of the room.

October 3

Charles called Momma again. He won't say where he is staying.

October 5

Momma goes out every night after supper to look for Charles. She walks from 104th Street on Broadway to 72nd Street on Broadway. Sometimes I walk with her. We haven't seen Charles. He must know that we walk every night looking for him and so he stays inside.

October 7

Miss A., the college adviser, and the principal all said I should take the PSAT, the Preliminary Scholastic Aptitude Test. They said it would be given sometime in December. They said it would cost $2.50. I asked them what the test would test. Miss A. gave me the best answer. She said, You.

October 8

Edgar's father came tonight for the first time in a long time. He was drunk. Momma didn't want to let him in but he said he had a present for Edgar. When she opened the door, he didn't have a present. He had a bottle of wine. Momma looked too tired to fight and so she let him sit down. For the first time he looked at Harriet and me, and Momma didn't like it.

Momma said he couldn't stay. Momma said the investigators were making night visits and throwing people off of welfare if they found a man in the room. Edgar's father poured himself a glass of wine. Edgar was within two feet of him but he didn't look at Edgar. Edgar got closer and tugged at his pants but he still didn't pick Edgar up.

Momma screamed out, Pick him up you son of a bitch or get the hell out of here!

Edgar's father picked up the wine bottle like he was going to hit Momma with it but Momma didn't seem frightened. Edgar's father got up and left.

I am getting frightened of how quick the days go by and we still haven't moved. The bathtub still doesn't work. I still have to sponge bathe. I don't like standing in the middle of the room naked washing myself. I want to be behind a shower curtain with a lot of stripes, hidden, soaping myself, letting the warm, clean water flow all over me and picking up a thick towel to wipe myself, in private, without drunks pounding on the door.

Doesn't Momma know this? Why does she stay here in this building? I am sure she could find a place if she wanted to, other people do. F.L. on the 4th floor moved out to Brooklyn. F.L. said Brooklyn is terrible. She said her rooms were inspected by the welfare department and somebody must have paid off somebody because the walls were cracked in her rooms and the gas stove was broken and the stoop to the building was broken. But she had 5 rooms, F.L. told Momma. F.L. told Momma to move. What is your block like in Brooklyn? Momma asked F.L. She said, Worse than this because you expect it to be better. Brooklyn is going to be bad, F.L. said, a lot of people are moving from here to Brooklyn.

Momma said, I don't know Brooklyn.

Do you think the people who live in Brooklyn know where they are at? F.L. said to Momma, it's like the bible says, we are strangers in a strange dirty land. Momma said, We'll visit you and then see what the vacancies look like.

In bed Harriet said to me, I think I am going to have a baby.

How do you know? I whispered. Harriet said the blood didn't come this month like it always does. That's a sign.

Who will you tell? I asked Harriet.

I don't know, Harriet said, I just don't want the baby to die like Momma's baby died.

Does R. know? I asked Harriet. He said he never puts anything on when we do it. Will he marry you? I asked Harriet. First I'll have a baby and go on welfare, Harriet said, then we can talk about getting married.

But you're too young to have your own case, I said to Harriet.

Not if I have a baby.

Where did you hear that rule?

It is a rule, Harriet said.

Momma won't let you live by yourself. She'll make you lose the baby.

Not if I have it long enough so it cant be lost.

I think you should tell Momma, I said to Harriet. You have to see a doctor.

What good will it do if Momma knows? She will only scream, Harriet said. Momma doesn't lift a finger, Harriet said, she acts so tired as though she has a ten room house to clean and yet this place is filthy, even when we clean it, it gets dirty in five minutes, it will be like this from now on.

You have to see a doctor, I said to Harriet.

I will, Harriet said, when the baby is ready to come out. Harriet stopped talking and went to sleep. I put my hand on her stomach and couldn't feel anything. I don't believe Harriet will have her baby. That will be doing all over again what Momma did.

Tonight Momma told the landlord she will not pay him any rent until the toilet is fixed and kept clean.

October 14

The landlady keeps bothering Momma for the rent money. The landlady says she will get an eviction notice. Momma says to go ahead. Momma said she will pay her rent when the toilet is fixed. The landlady screamed at Momma that the pigs break it ten minutes after it is fixed. They don't know how to flush a toilet, the landlady shouted. The pigs, the pigs, the landlady shouted, I keep a clean house and the pigs wreck it, drunks and pigs. Momma said if you want your money, fix the toilet. The landlady said I will tell your investigator. Do it, Momma said.

I wish Momma wouldn't fight to have the toilet fixed. I wish we would just run from the house and leave everything behind. The welfare will give us everything we need for a new apartment.

October 15

Harriet is not pregnant. She started to bleed. She said she hopes the bleeding never stops.

October 25

I studied Miss A.'s face today. Is being a teacher what she wanted of life when she was a girl? Miss A. was talking in class about Nathaniel Hawthorne. Miss A. spends more time talking about Hawthorne than anyone else. She said Hawthorne loved his family. Miss A. said Hawthorne died in his sleep, peacefully, but alone in a hotel room far from his family. He had become ill and lost his great strength. His best friend had died only a short time before him. Miss A. talked about Nathaniel Hawthorne as though he was a member of her own family. She said some of the greatest men in America stood around the simple grave where he was buried on a slope called Sleepy Hollow. She said Longfellow, Whittier and Emerson were there. She said the sun was shining and the birds were singing. Her face seemed to go back into history. Miss A. had told us that she was born in New England. Then her family came to New York. She stumbled and said she grew up in *Whitechester* and then changed it to Westchester.

Miss A. is a miss. She has no husband.

Is there a man that she loves? Would she give up teaching if she got married? If she got married it would be in a big church. Her family would come to fill the church. I can imagine her walking down the aisle. She would walk on roses without crushing them. She would look straight ahead and see only the future. In the evening she would make herself naked for her husband. She would be like an island that no one had ever been to before. An island of tall trees and hills, flowers and a sea where the water washed against shining sand. She would take her husband into her. Her legs around him. Her mouth finding his. She would lay this way with him, her body as open as a field. She would look straight up into the face of her husband. This is what I think a woman should do with a man, look at him. Men seem to be so afraid. Momma says men *are* afraid. She says they seem to be frightened of life. She says men are happiest when they are boys. Being a man Momma says is too much for men. Momma says men worshipped the Virgin Mary more than they ever did Jesus. Everything is done for the Virgin Mary, Momma says, the whole church is for the Virgin Mary. The church should be for men, Momma said. Momma said all this just talking, not to me or Harriet but just talking as she sometimes does when she remembers that she has a life.

Is Miss A. happy in what she does? Is this where she wants her life to be, in this classroom telling us about the death of Nathaniel Hawthorne? What more will her life be before she dies? Teachers always seem so alone. They don't seem to have lives. Where does Miss A. go at night when she leaves this school? Once in a while Miss A. tells us about a play she saw on Broadway, a movie she liked. Did she go alone? Does she make her own breakfast? Does she eat breakfast at the counter of a drugstore? Does she buy her dresses at Macys? Does she wait to leave this classroom so that she can start her own life again? Is this her real life here? I hope it is. I want Miss A. to be real. I want her to believe herself every word that she says to us, not like most of the teachers here who seem to have to force themselves to talk, who can't wait for the bell, who rush for the subway, who never see you.

I like the college catalogues Miss A. has shown me. They tell you who the teachers are. They tell you where each teacher went to school. What they did. But no catalogue can tell me the things I want to know about Miss A. I think its because I listen so much to everything Miss A. says that I want to know so much about her. When I read a book I don't care about the writer. I only care about the story. But Miss A. is my teacher. My only *teacher* in this school. I think I want Miss A. to give me more than she can give me, I think I want her to give me safe passage but she can't, no one can. Except that I think we live easier when we know other people care if we live or die and how we live and die.

I know I will never forget Miss A. because what I have learned from her so far can never be forgotten.

October 27

The attendance officer came about Charles.

October 28

The teacher in the science class handed out a list of questions to us. The questions were about sex and drugs. She said we did not have to put our names on the question sheet. She said some people were making a study. Everybody in the class lied. I said I used heroin, I smoked cigarettes, I had intercourse 9 times a week, I hated my mother, I hated my father, my father's profession was a drug pusher and my younger sister was addicted to drugs. Then when I read over what I had done, it seemed to me that these might be true answers for a lot of people I know and for about three or four people in my class.

October 30

Mrs. B. told Momma that she saw Charles on Broadway and 83rd Street.

October 31

I went with Momma to Broadway and 83rd Street. Momma walked on one side of Broadway and I walked on the other side of Broadway. We didn't see Charles.

November 2

Edgar's father came by to borrow $5 from Momma. He stayed the night.

November 5

Momma and Harriet had another big fight. Harriet came home at 11:30. Harriet doesn't answer Momma when they fight. She just listens or lays down on the bed. Momma hits Harriet but Harriet doesn't cry. Momma thinks Harriet is still a little girl. On the outside she is. But inside she has been a woman for over 2 months. I think Harriet says to herself everytime Momma yells at her, I'm making out. Momma doesn't seem to know or want to know.

November 7

The 40 year old investigator came by. The last time he spent 2 minutes with Momma. He just looked at Mommas receipt. This time he started to get up to go and Momma stopped him. Just open that book again, Momma said. The investigator did just what Momma asked.

Edgar needs a snowsuit and boots, Momma said. Harriet needs a winter jacket. Momma said I needed a winter coat and a jacket and boots. The investigator said he couldn't give a winter coat and jacket. Momma said she needed a winter coat and boots. The investigator wrote it all down in the book.

Momma said, How soon will we get the clothing? The investigator said he had to check the case record and his supervisor would have to approve it. Momma said, You all act like its your money.

The investigator stood up and said, If somebody told me before I took this job that I could give away money like I do I would have told them they were crazy.

Momma said to the investigator, What's crazy about giving a winter jacket to a girl so she can go to school?

The investigator didn't mention an apartment and Momma didnt either.

November 10

The heat stopped today. The landlord said the boiler broke. Momma turned on all of the gas burners. We sat around in our jackets. I went to sleep with my shoes on. I need a bath. I want a warm bath. I want to sit in a bathtub. I just want to soak. I feel so dirty. The hot water doesn't come out. I said to Momma that we should stand in front of the house or even lay down on the sidewalk. I said if we put blankets on the sidewalk the TV news would come and take pictures of us. I said TV does that. We could get an apartment then. Momma said she wouldnt sleep on the sidewalk for nobody. I said its not for nobody but for us. Momma told me to shut up. She hates when I say something with sense in it. Momma can't stand that. It makes her yell. Momma has to know that we can't go on staying in this room. All the rooms that must have been closets where there is only space for a bed, these rooms are now filled with drug addicts and sick people. The sick ones lay in their beds and get the boys to run to Broadway for them to buy a chicken and they eat it for two days, throwing the bones in the hallway because some of them cant get out of their beds. If you leave your door open for a minute the addicts steal anything. Momma left some groceries on the folding table for a minute and it was gone. They stole our pots and pans and Momma rushed down to the welfare office to get an emergency check. Somebody took Edgar's old snowsuit. A lot of men are coming here now who have been in prison, I heard the landlord say. Now there is a policeman on check day who stands in the hallway. Somebody said the landlord gives the policeman $25. But there are still robberies. Momma pays her rent immediately on check day and then she rushes to the A&P to buy food before anybody can steal her money.

There is slush in the street. When I come home from school and walk into the building I feel as though a rat has crawled inside of me and is chewing his way out.

I fight with Momma now. I tell Momma we have to move. Is it really possible that Momma feels she has to stay in this building as some kind of punishment? There is nothing Momma has done so bad in her life for this kind of punishment. Momma sees nobody except Edgar's father. She doesn't drink like some of the mothers. She doesn't stay out until 2 in the morning. She doesn't put us in the hallway while she takes men into her bed. She tries to make meals for us. The welfare will pay rent anywhere we move. We don't have to worry about the money. The welfare will pay almost any rent and it doesnt come off our food money. Momma knows all this. Yet she stays here. I wish somebody could tell me why. Doesn't the investigator who comes here see that we can no longer live here? Can't he find one more room for us? Don't they have laws at the welfare building?

Each check day everybody lines up in the hallway to give the landlord and the landlady the welfare rent money. I am sure that chickens waiting to be killed in a chicken store are treated better than we are here and have more protection until they die.

The chickens must be clean for the people who will eat them.

November 12

The investigator told Momma that Edgar was given a snowsuit a year ago. Momma said, He has grown, he is alive, he grows, and his snowsuit was stolen. The investigator said he will check again with his supervisor.

November 15

Charles doesn't telephone Momma. We have no news from him. Now I believe it is possible for a 12 year old boy to do what Charles is doing.

November 24

Thanksgiving Day.

November 27

Momma received a letter from the school saying Charles was suspended.

November 28

Momma took me to Broadway to look for Charles. We started this time on 96th Street. We went into the cafeteria where the drug addicts hang out. They sit in the chairs half asleep. They talk to each other but no one listens. Momma had a cup of coffee. I had a Pepsi-Cola and a toasted English muffin. Most of the addicts looked about 19 or 20. We didn't see anyone Charles' age. Momma said that if she sat there all day she was sure Charles would walk in. I said she could do it. I would stay home from school and look after Edgar. Momma said she would see. We went out of the cafeteria and looked at the people sitting on the benches between the traffic on Broadway. Most of the people are old and they don't talk to each other either. They just sit and stare and hope to see some excitement. I stared again at the big buildings on Broadway and down the streets leading to Riverside Drive. Certainly in one of the buildings there was a vacancy where Momma could move in. I said this to Momma. She said to keep an eye on vacancy signs.

On 91st Street I saw a vacancy sign. It looked like a hotel. I said to Momma, Lets go in. It was a very big building with two elevators. There was a man behind a marble desk. The lobby was big and dark. I saw a broken Coca Cola machine. The man at the desk said he had a vacancy. We followed him into the elevator. Two of the buttons were broken. There was writing all over the elevator doors. He took us down a long curving hallway. You could feel the dirt under your feet. The doors had complicated numbers like 105EA. In the middle of the long hallway he opened a door with a key. The room smelled. There was no sheet on the mattress. There were big watermarks on the mattress. It was a single bed.

There was a chest with one drawer pulled out. The window-shade was pulled down and torn. The man said the toilet was at the end of the hallway. He said there was a community kitchen where we could cook. Momma said, Can we see the kitchen? The man took us into a big room with two, three stoves. There was a refrigerator with a heavy chain and lock around the handle. There were cupboards but nothing was in the cupboards. Momma said, How many people cook here? The man said, About 15 families. How many use the toilet? Momma asked. All that have to, the man said. We went back to the room. The minute you stepped into the room you saw the wall. There was no closet. Momma asked him the rent. The man said $19.75 a week, we provide the sheets and blankets. Is it for you two? the man asked. No, Momma said, for me and four children. Why didn't you say so? the man said, we don't have rooms for families that large except on the third floor and they are all taken. I didn't see any children. A drunken man got into the elevator with us. He kept saying to me, Bless you, bless you, and when he tried to put his hand on me Momma stopped him.

The street almost looked clean when we got outside. I wanted to run down the street to the Hudson River and feel something clean.

You see, Momma said to me, this is what most of the empty rooms are like, would you want to live here?

No, I said to Momma.

This is a welfare building, Momma said, you can smell them, every single person in the building must be on welfare, nobody else could pay the rents or stand for that kitchen.

We don't have to live in this building, I said to Momma, but there must be some clean buildings.

You can think that, Momma said, but if its welfare money, there aren't any clean buildings.

We walked very slowly to 86th Street. I looked at the faces on the sidewalk. They all looked so tired and worn out. The faces of the white people looked bewildered, as though they had been captured by a strange army.

We saw a lot of boys Charles' age on the sidewalk. We watched two boys talking to some older men and the boys went off with them. Is that what Charles does?

Momma said, Lets go to 72nd Street. In the park near 72nd Street we saw the benches filled with men. Momma said they were all homosexuals or drug addicts. I said to Momma, Why don't the police do something? All the jails would be filled in ten minutes, Momma said. Momma said, Lets sit here and wait to see if Charles will come by.

We found an empty space on a bench where two men tried to stare us away. Men got up from the different benches to talk to each other and then they left the park. We sat in the park for an hour. We didnt see Charles. Momma said, Lets go into the Automat. We crossed 72nd Street and went into the Automat which was very bright. Momma got some coffee and I got a piece of apple pie. Momma looked around the Automat. It was filled with old men and old women and they sat at the tables as though they had no other place in the world to go. The old people all looked so old. Some of them must be on welfare and live in buildings like the one we had looked at. No wonder they sit as long as they can in the Automat.

Momma drank her coffee slowly. I offered Momma half of my apple pie. Momma looked at everyone coming through the door. Momma didn't talk. She stared at her coffee and the door. We were so far away from 104th Street that it seemed it didn't exist. Here everybody ate at a table and sat on a chair. The cups and glasses were shining clean where you went for coffee and water. It only cost 10 cents to sit down and drink your coffee. We could afford that even on our welfare check. What I was thinking to myself and wondering if I dared to say it to Momma was, Why can't we live like other people even if we do get a welfare check? But Momma wasn't a stupid person. She had finished high school. Still I never saw her read anything. She almost never watched television. She almost never talked.

Momma finished her coffee and said, We wont find Charles this way.

November 30

The boiler is supposed to be working tonight, Mrs. A.M. said that if the boiler isn't working she will set fire to her mattress.

December 2

Harriet told me tonight that she doesn't want a baby now. Harriet said, That would only keep me on welfare for the rest of my life. Don't you see what happened to Momma? Harriet said, first she had you, then me, then Charles, and when she had Edgar she was finished. She can't work, she can't find a big enough apartment, she can't do anything but just stay alive. Momma will get fat like the other women in this house. She will sit in a chair and never get out of it. Harriet said that she told R. that if he wants to do it to her now he has to wear something.

December 3

Three policemen came to the door tonight and asked Momma if she has heard anything from Charles. Momma said no. The police said a bunch of young pushers were selling to kids in the elementry school and junior high schools. The police gave Momma a number and told her to call them immediately if she saw Charles.

Momma said to the police that the toilet wasn't working on our floor. The police said that was none of their business and they left.

December 5

I saw Charles on Broadway. He was on 108th Street. He looked at me and was going to run. Then he didn't.

Charles looks 10 years older. It is impossible to believe that he is still 12 years old. I asked Charles where he was living. He said he couldn't say. I asked him how he was living. He said he couldnt say. I told him about the police coming to 104th Street. He said, Did Momma tell them anything? I said she had nothing to say. Charles said that was good. I asked Charles if he was still using drugs. He said no, but I think he was lying. I asked him if he was selling drugs. He said no. I asked him if he was staying with the white man. He said no. Then Charles said, I got to go. I asked him if he had a telephone where we could call him. He said no. I saw a policeman across the street. I didn't know if I should call out for the policeman to hold Charles. I didn't. Charles said again he had to go. Where does he go? What does he do?

I told Momma I saw Charles. She screamed at me that I should have knocked him down to the sidewalk and held him there.

I said I couldn't. Momma screamed at me because I didn't find out where Charles lives. I told Momma he wouldn't tell me. You should have made him tell you, Momma yelled. Momma yelled at me until we all fell asleep.

December 8

The boiler is finally fixed. There is hot water and heat. But the toilet is still broken. We are supposed to have inspectors go through the building but nobody has seen them. I wish the inspectors wore badges or special hats so that we would know who they are. This way the landlord can give them money for seeing nothing. It is impossible for there to be any improvements made in this building. The walls to our room can't be stretched. No toilet can be added to our room, no bathtub. There is no room in our one room for a closet.

December 9

The investigator stopped by today. He asked Momma if Charles was home. He told Momma that Charles would have to go off the budget if he wasn't staying in the house. Momma tried to say that Charles was only away for a few days. The investigator said he received a letter from somebody living in the building and the letter said Charles wasn't living with Momma. Who sent you the letter? Momma asked. The investigator said it wasn't signed. The investigator said he heard from the police that Charles had run away. The investigator said drugs was getting serious around the schools and the police were trying to get the pushers. I can't think of Charles as a pusher. The investigator said he would take Charles off the budget and Momma would get less on her check.

December 10

A man knocked on our door today. He said he was from the Public Health service. He asked about Harriet. Momma said, What do you want with my daughter? The man asked Harriet if she knew R. Harriet said yes. The man said Harriet would need an examination. For what? Momma almost screamed out. The man kept very cool. He said R. had gonohrea and he mentioned Harriet's name and it would be best if she was examined to see if she was infected. No, god damn you, Momma yelled. The man said it was important for Harriet to be examined. Her whole system could be infected if she wasn't examined and treated. Momma hit her hands on the table. She didn't even look at Harriet. I could see she wanted to tear at Harriet's hair but she didn't dare do it in front of the man. The man said Harriet would only have to take some pills if there was anything wrong with her. Well? the man said. Momma said, Where does she go? The man gave Momma a card. Momma said, Does this go into any kind of record? It's a health record, the man said, and its confidential. Like everything else, Momma said. The man said its for her own good. What happens to this R. boy? Momma said. The man said that wasn't up to him. He said he could be a police problem since Harriet was so young. For her or for him? Momma asked. Probably for him, the man said. The man left.

Momma got up from the chair and slapped Harriet so that she fell backward on the bed. Harriet didn't cry.

That's why you stayed out of school, Momma yelled at her. Momma went for Harriet again. She pulled her hair and slapped her again. Harriet still didn't cry. Momma started crying. She sat down on the chair and cried. Momma said, You can make us all sick. Harriet said, I don't want to do that. Momma said, When did you start with him? Harriet just said, Some time ago. Momma said, You're only 13. Momma said, Do you know what gonohrea is? Harriet said no. Momma said its an infection for whores, not for 13 year olds. Momma said, Its like the man said, it can ruin everything inside of you. One person gives it to another person. Thats what happened here, he kept giving it to everybody, you included.

Harriet said, I felt a burning in me but I didn't know what it was. Then you got it, Momma said. When did you feel the burning? Three days ago, Harriet said. Why didn't you tell me? I just thought it was a baby going away, Harriet said. A baby going away, Momma screamed.

Isnt that the way you get babies? Harriet said.

Shut up, Momma said, or I'll kill you.

Momma turned to me and said, Are you doing it to?

I said no.

Momma said we all had to go for an examination. You get it from toilet seats, Momma said.

Do you feel a burning? Momma asked me.

I said no.

We'll all go tomorrow, Momma said.

Harriet put some water on her face.

Momma gave Harriet one more slap which seemed to be all of the strength she had left.

In bed Harriet said to me, What do you know about it?

I said we had a teacher who gave a talk on it. I said it was like the man said, it was an infection, and you mostly got it the way she had gotten it from R. Can it kill you? Harriet asked me. Not any more, I said, but not too long ago it made you so sick that you wanted to be dead. Will it stop me from having babies? Harriet asked. Sometimes it can, I said. But today they have a pill for everything, Harriet said. R. told me he made out with 15 girls. Do they all have it?

It burns, Harriet said, it burns. I just thought it would go away.

December 11

Momma and myself are all right. Harriet has to take pills. Momma complained to the doctor about the toilet in our building. He said there was nothing he could do. He told Momma to call the Department of Buildings.

December 15

Harriet told me the burning is starting to go away.

December 17

Momma says the paper plates kept us all from getting infected.

December 18

I am going to take the PSAT test in the morning at 9 A.M. Miss A. said that I couldn't study for the test, because the questions asked would be a sum of what I have learned up until tonight. How much have I learned? Is it enough for me to pass a test that may make it possible for me to go to college?

Miss A. said I shouldn't be frightened of the test. I shouldn't see it as a wall I have to climb. She said I should see the test as an acknowledgement of what I know. Language is most important on the test, Miss A. told me. To know words, their meaning, their relationship, to know what you read. If this is the test, then I will go to it confidently. I am only afraid of history. I seem to have so little history of my own. I need more history than I can get from books. I wish we had little parades like they have in small towns where everybody goes to the curb and the people in the town beat on drums and blow bugles and march proudly. School should be that way. But my school is like a city with all of its wires struck down by lightning.

So tomorrow morning I will be tested. I will take Miss A.'s advice. I will be confident. I will sharpen my pencil. I will forget for three hours the landlady of this building, the screams, this room that should never be our home. I will forget it all because the test has to do with a world that doesn't even know any of this really exists.

Momma said to me tonight, How come you're not studying for the test?

Harriet said, You're *not* paying money to take a test! The cost of the test is $2.50. Momma gave me the money for the test, saying she didn't want anybody else to pay for it.

December 19

I sat for three hours taking the PSAT test. I was never more alone in my life.

Harriet told me R. was arrested because the girls he saw were under 16.

December 20

Momma emptied her purse on the chest and I saw a photograph I had never seen before. It was Momma standing with a boy. Momma looked about 16 or 17. The boy looked the same age. He was taller than Momma. He had straight hair. He was smiling in the picture. He had his arm around Momma. I looked at the picture and then I looked at my face in the mirror above the kitchen sink. I could see where I looked like Momma. But I couldn't see myself in the boy's picture.

December 22

Harriet said we should try to clean up the room for Christmas. We started sweeping the floor and getting the kitchen clean. Harriet washed down the refrigerator. I washed the stove and the sink. We sprayed roach powder over the bottom of the refrigerator and the bottom of the sink. Harriet washed all of the knives and forks standing in the sink. I hung up a calendar I got from the bank on Broadway. I sprayed the room with a deodorizer. Momma was downstairs. We made the beds. Maybe the place would stay clean until Christmas. But not the building.

December 25

This is Christmas Day. Momma gave me two books, Harriet gave me a bottle of cologne. I gave Momma a scarf. I gave Harriet fingernail polish. I gave Edgar a toy duck to pull.

December 28

I have an English assignment that I have to turn in after the holidays. Miss A. asked us to write a biography of our mother and father. Miss A. kept the class very quiet one day when she told us about a Civil War black colonel the white officers wanted out of the army. They were ready to discharge the colonel saying that he was too weak and too sick to stay in the army and get more promotions. The black colonel rode horseback from a town in Ohio to Washington, D.C. to prove that he wasn't sick. She gives us homework and marks our papers. Most of the other teachers give homework but they never mark the papers.

I told Momma that I had to write a report about my father. Momma said, What is there to write if he hasnt been your father, if you never saw him? I said to Momma that he was older now and he might be somebody, he might be a lawyer or a doctor. Momma said she hasn't seen my father since the time she was pregnant. I said to Momma, Never? She said it's not like Edgar's father who comes around once in awhile. I never saw your father after I was pregnant. He didn't try to get in touch with you? I asked Momma. No. Did you ever try to find him? I asked Momma. The welfare department tried but they couldn't locate him, and that was a time when they were trying to find fathers.

Is there anything you can tell me that I can write about? I asked Momma. Just write what you want to, Momma said, those teachers don't know the difference.

This is what I wrote:

I do not know my father. I never saw my father. My father never came to see me when I was born. He never came to see when I was a baby. My father never bought me a toy, a snow-suit, a doll, a dress, an ice cream cone, a book. I do not know if my father is short or tall. If he is alive or dead. I do not know in what part of the world my father is living. He may be in the South. He may be around the corner from me. He may be in jail. He may be a scientist. He may not even know that he has a child. He may not know that I am his daughter. I do not know how to tell him that he has a daughter. The welfare department has been searching for my father for 15 years. They have never been able to speak to him. He may want to pay for my support but the welfare department has not been able to find my father. I do not believe we would be living in this building if my father knew I was his daughter. No father would permit such a thing. There are no *fathers in this building. That is why the women live with three and four and five and even more children in one room that was meant for only one person. A real father would tear down these walls. The building would not exist except for the old people in it, the drunks and the addicts. They need someplace to sleep when they are not in a hospital or a jail. I wish my father could see this place. I wonder what he would do. No one else seems to be able to do anything. But the father of a child might find a way to do something about the way his daughter lives in this building.*

I cannot write about my father. He does not exist. But I do have a father who exists. Maybe the welfare department will find him. He will find that he has a daughter who is ready to have a father.

December 29

I tore up what I wrote except to put it here.

December 31

Happy new year! This is what it said on the card Charles mailed to Momma. Momma searched and searched the card for an address but there was none.

January 3

Harriet said all the burning is gone. She is still taking pills.

January 5

I reminded Momma that we have been living in this room for almost one year. I saw her face change almost as though she didn't believe what I had said.

January 7

It will be a year very soon.

January 8

I am glad I discovered the library on West 100th Street.

January 10

A new investigator came today. She asked Momma if Charles was back home. Momma said no. The investigator said then he'll have to be off the budget. This investigator doesn't seem to be afraid to be in the room. She unbuttoned her coat and lit a cigarette. She offered Momma a cigarette. She didn't open her black book. Momma looked at her to see what she was after. Momma says the job of all the investigators she has seen is to get you off of welfare. They look for anything to close your case. Like a mans hat hanging in the room. Or a rent receipt that you can't find. Or if you don't keep an appointment they set up for you. Or if there is a question they ask you which you don't want to answer. Or if they come to your door twice and you're not at home they'll close your case and say "Whereabouts unknown," even if they know you can't live two days without your welfare check.

The new investigator said to Momma, I want to find your boy, I don't believe a 12 year boy should be away from home the way Charles is.

Momma said, If you find him the court will only put him in some kind of an institution that's like a jail.

The investigator said, Does that mean you know where Charles is?

Momma said, I don't know where Charles is, he's in the street somewhere. He sent me a Christmas card with no return address on it.

Can I see the card? the investigator asked. Momma showed her the card. I just wanted to see from what post office station it was mailed.

Are you a policewoman? Momma asked.

No, I'm not a policewoman.

Why do you want to find Charles? Momma asked.

I just got your case, the investigator said. I read about Charles running away, then coming back, then running away. The running away will have to stop, the investigator said, if Charles is ever going to find out who he is and what he can do.

Who will tell him that? Momma said, you?

Did he find it out from you? the investigator asked Momma.

For a minute I thought Momma was going to throw the investigator out.

Nobody can tell Charles what he is, Momma said, speaking very slowly, holding each word like you hold a yolk when you want to separate it from the whites, nobody can tell Charles because nobody wants him to know.

Why do you say that? the investigator asked.

I had four fathers for my four children. Not one of them was a real man, Momma said.

The investigator said, Do you want the children to leave the room?

Momma said, They know what I'm talking about even if they cant put it into words. They can listen to anything you want to ask.

What do you mean by not a real man? the investigator asked.

Except for the first one who didn't know he was a father, Momma said, they were all afraid to be a father. That scared them more than anything else in this world. When I told each of them except the first one that he was going to be a father they looked at me like they were going to kill me. Two of them said they would kill me if I told the welfare where they lived. They stopped coming around. They took off for new neighborhoods. They never came by to see if their baby was living or dead. They never came to the hospital. The father of Edgar comes around. But not to see his baby. He comes to see me and I don't mind because I need a man once in awhile and I'm not in the mind to go looking for one.

Does Edgars father give any support? the investigator asked Momma.

He lives off the street, Momma said, from day to day. One day he'll get busted and I won't see him again.

Do you see any other kind of men? the investigator asked, someone you might think of marrying?

Who's going to marry a welfare client with four babies? Momma asked, would you?

I liked the investigator because she stayed cool.

The investigator said to Momma, Has anybody been able to tell you anything about Charles?

One of the neighbors saw him on 83rd Street. My girl saw him on 107th Street. And we had the card.

Do you have a picture of him? the investigator asked.

Momma gave the investigator a photograph of Charles standing in front of the house on 118th Street.

I want it back, Momma said.

I'm out on the street a lot, the investigator said, maybe I'll see Charles.

If you see him, what will you say? Momma asked.

That depends, the investigator said.

Nobody alive would know what to say to Charles, Momma said, he'd have to be put in a running stream of water and held there until he was washed clean. He's been made dirty. More dirty than any 12 year old boy has a right to be. You look for him, Momma said, you look, then you use your words, then you come back to me and tell me what they did to Charles and then I want you to get down on your knees if Charles didn't listen to your words. You just don't know where you're at, Momma said to the investigator, you don't know.

That's your opinion, the investigator said.

I wish it was just my opinion, Momma said, I wish it was my opinion alone, I wish that, I wish that.

Is it this building then? the investigator asked Momma.

You're white, Momma said, and you like to lay blame, you think laying blame is the answer. No, Momma said, it's not this building because this building wouldn't exist without a lot of other people wanting it to exist. This building serves a purpose, Momma said, and let me hear you say what it is.

What purpose does this building serve? the investigator asked Momma.

To make welfare like dirt, Momma said, you don't want welfare to be any different and nobody else does, otherwise nobody would pay a nickels rent for this building or any other building where welfare people live.

There was a silence in the room.

I could see Harriet was almost holding her breath. Edgar was pulling on the toy duck I bought him. The investigator lit another cigarette. The striking of her match broke the silence. Momma was waiting for her to speak.

The investigator said, I hope you're wrong though I think you're right. But that doesn't mean everybody feels the way you think they do.

Everybody, Momma said. On this, everybody, Momma said.

Then what am I doing here? the investigator said.

Momma said, Doing a job, whatever they tell you the job is.

The investigator said to Momma, Do you know what they told me when I took this job? I wasn't to interfere with mothers on welfare, I wasn't to go into any of their problems, because the welfare mothers would just suck me down into their own problems that didnt have any chance of ever getting settled, the investigator said. I was told, the investigator said, not to talk to you about the father of your children, birth control, getting a job but just to leave you alone, because some people saw you as belonging to some kind of holy poor that shouldn't be touched, disturbed, stirred up, made to answer to many questions. Is that the way you want it? the investigator said.

Momma said, My life isn't going to be solved by words.

The investigator said, Is it all right with you if I look for Charles?

Momma said, You do what your job is.

The investigator put out her cigarette. She said to Momma, If I find Charles I'll tell you first.

When the investigator left Momma said, I hope you heard it all.

January 12

What stopped Momma from being a teacher?

January 13

I walked into the library today on 100th Street. I finally filled out an application for a library card. The librarian seemed surprised that I could write my name and address so easily but she quickly hid her surprise when I asked her if I could take out books right away. I was able to take two books home. I chose the life of Isadora Duncan and *Little Women.*

January 15

The landlord is being taken into court. I went with Momma to the court. We sat in the second row. The people from the democratic club want the people evicted from our building on 104th Street. The lawyer from the club says there are too many people in one room and it's against the law. The judge doesn't look very interested in the case. Miss A.V. from the 5th floor spoke in court. The lawyer had her tell that she has 5 children in one room, plus herself, with no toilet or bathtub. The judge asked her how many people use the toilet and bathtub in the hallway and she said, None because it's always broke. The lawyer had Mrs. W.D. from the 4th floor speak. She said she had 4 children. The judge asked her the same questions and how much rent she paid. Mrs. W.D. said $21.85 a week. The lawyer said it was inhuman for families to live in single rooms. The judge said a lot of things were inhuman in this world. The judge said to the lawyer, If I should evict these people, where will they go to live? Do you have apartments for them to move into? The lawyer said no. The judge said, Do you want me to put them in the street? The lawyer said no. The judge said, Then what do you want me to do? The lawyer said, We thought this case could influence the city to find housing for these families. The judge said, But you are in my courtroom, I have to make the decision. Do you want these people in the street or do you want them to stay where they are until they can find housing? The lawyer said, We didn't come into court to put them into the street.

The judge said, Then we'll hold this over to see what happens with vacant housing. The judge said there were one million people in New York City living in bad housing. The judge said when he was a student he rented a room in Greenwich

Village for $3 a week. He bought a gallon of paint and painted his room. He bought a can of roach powder. He bought some washing soap and washed out the bathroom on his top floor. He said he went to the dime store and bought a pair of paper drapes for 89 cents. He said to the lawyer, Why don't you rent a room in one of these buildings for a week or month just to see and feel what it is because I don't think you know, otherwise you wouldn't have brought these people into court with some kind of understanding that this court had the power to find them fresh clean housing.

January 17

It is one year since we have been living in this room. Momma said it is not possible. But we all know that it is.

January 21

The SPCC came to the door to ask Momma if she knew anything about the thin girl on the top floor who looks white but who is black. I know her. She looks 16 but she is 21 and she has 5 babies. Momma said she didn't know her. Momma asked what was wrong. The SPCC woman said her 6 year old boy ran away from home and was found on Columbus Avenue and 90th Street by the police and taken to the Childrens Center. The SPCC woman said the boy whose name is A. was not wearing any shoes at the time he was picked up. The boy was wandering around the street and acted like a frightened animal when the police started to talk to him. She said the mother hasn't been to the Childrens Center since he was picked up and that was 10 days ago. So much happens in this house without anyone knowing about it. I went upstairs to see M.S. because I used to babysit for her and I thought maybe there was something I could do for her.

When I walked in M.S. was sitting in a chair and she looked dirty. Her hair wasn't combed. She had no shoes on and her feet were dirty. Her dress didn't look right. Her eyes looked all worn out. But M.S. sometimes has a nice face. The man who stays with her is terrible. He almost caused a riot on 105th Street when an investigator stopped to talk to him.

I asked M.S. if there was anything I could do for her. For a minute she didn't answer me. I went over to her babies. The babies looked like they had not been eating. Their flesh was dry and their faces looked thin. I didn't see any food on the shelves above the counter. I looked in the refrigerator. There was a quart of milk but it smelled stale. M.S. didn't seem able to move. I went downstairs to get Momma. M.S. looked to sick for me to talk to.

Momma came into the room and looked at the babies. Momma said, They need food. Momma asked M.S. if she had any money. M.S. opened her pocketbook and there was a lot of money. Momma told M.S. she was taking $10. Momma took the $10 and told me what to buy. She said I should find Harriet to help me carry the food. Momma started cleaning up all the stuff the babies left on the floor. When we got back with the food the room looked cleaner but M.S. still didn't move from the table. Momma learned that the 6 year old had walked out of the house 2 weeks ago. How could a boy that young walk the streets alone for even 2 days before he was picked up?

Maybe no one looked at him.

Momma said she would call her investigator and see what could be done or had to be done for M.S.

A psychiatrist came in an emergency to see M.S. He was a short man with glasses and he kept saying somebody should clean off the table. Momma and me stayed in the room during the examination. He asked M.S. her name. He asked M.S. the day of the week. He asked for the names of her children. He asked her to add 5 and 7. He asked her how many legs there were on a table. Then he said M.S. was able to function in the community. He said there was no need at this time to send her to Bellevue. But she won't go see her baby, the investigator said. A lot of women won't, the psychiatrist said. When we find out why she won't, then maybe she'll go. Right now my guess is that something happened that makes her feel to ashamed to see her son.

Momma and the investigator began talking quietly to M.S.

In a few minutes she began talking herself and thanked them for buying food and cleaning up the room.

Momma asked M.S. why she wouldn't walk across the park to see her boy. M.S. was silent. Momma asked her again. M.S. started to talk in a very tired voice. She told Momma that one of the fathers of her children was staying in the room with her. Two nights before her boy ran away, she woke up and she saw her boy with D. She said D. stuck his p. into her boy. She said all the time the father's hand was wrapped tight around the mouth of her boy. She said her boy was kicking hard and trying to fight. Then the father whispered something in the boy's ear and he became limp. M.S. said she then rushed out of bed and the father hit her in the face and she fell down. When she got up the father was gone and the boy was screaming.

M.S. said the father came over two days later. When the boy saw him he started screaming and he ran down the stairs.

Momma said she should pick up her boy. M.S. said she would when she stopped being tired. M.S. said she was going to move away. She heard about a building on the Lower East Side where they took in children and where welfare paid the rent. Momma took the address.

I don't think I want to live there if it is a building M.S. has heard about.

January 23

Miss C. and myself talked tonight. We had to talk in whispers because we were in the library. Miss C. is one of the librarians. She is so neat. Librarians must be the kindest, gentlest people in the entire world. Miss C. saw me looking at books in the stacks.

Are you looking for any special book? she asked me.

I said I was supposed to write a book report on *Giants In The Earth*.

It's a beautiful book, Miss C. said. Miss C. reached into racks and took down a copy of *Giants In The Earth*. She held the book in her hand for a minute and then handed it to me as though she was giving me something of her own, a gift that she wanted me to have. I would like to see the report you write on the book, Miss C. said.

I said I would show it to her.

I see you come in often, Miss C. said, do your brothers and sisters like to read to?

Sometimes, I said. I never remembered Charles reading a book.

Have you been to the 42nd Street library yet? Miss C. asked me. I said no.

You should go one day, Miss C. said, it is one of the largest libraries in the world. It has over 2 million books. Miss C. saw me look at her in surprise. You don't have to read all of the books, Miss C. said, and we both almost laughed. But go there one day, Miss C. said, go there and feel that it is your library, it is there for you, all those books were written for you even if you don't read them all.

January 25

M.S. moved without picking up her boy at the Childrens Center. The SPCC and M.S.'s investigator stopped in to see Momma. Momma gave them the address on the Lower East Side. The investigator said M.S. should be in a hospital and the children placed. Momma said the psychiatrist should also be in a hospital for saying M.S. was all right. The investigator said, He meant for the conditions under which she was living she was all right, the hospital would only be worse.

Momma said she learned from M.S. that D. whispered in the boys ear that if he made a noise he would cut his mothers throat and the throats of all of his brothers and sisters.

January 27

Momma went to the Lower East Side to the building where M.S. moved. Momma said M.S. looked sick. The boy was still at the Childrens Center. Momma said it was hard talking to M.S. Momma said she thinks M.S. should be in a hospital and the children should also be in a hospital. Momma said the children looked like they were starving. Momma gave them something to eat but M.S. wouldn't eat.

Momma asked me to write a letter to the Mayor. She said she heard the Mayor answers all letters in three days. Momma asked me to write that M.S. should be in a hospital and the children should be in a hospital because they were starving to death in New York City. Momma said she didn't trust the welfare investigator to do anything. I mailed the letter.

February 15

The minute I open the door to the library I feel warm. Where else do I have so many choices to make?

February 17

I brought my report on *Giants In The Earth* to show to Miss C. She was busy at the checkout desk when I came in. I wasn't going to bother her. But she called me over to the desk. I handed her the book report without saying anything. I didn't think she was going to read it in front of me. I stood there while she read it. She read slowly. I watched her eyes going across the sentences and sometimes I saw her smile.

It's beautiful, Miss C. said, beautiful, you read the book the way it was written.

Miss C. said, Now I am going to read *Giants In The Earth* again, I keep forgetting here in New York how people did go out to settle this country. It wasn't easy, Miss C. said. Miss C. speaks to me as though there is no question in her mind that I will not be able to understand every word that she says to me. That way of talking is the way I think my father would have spoken to me.

February 24

I think Momma must work out a plan for moving. She cannot depend on the welfare investigators. They always tell her the same story, the buildings they can send her to are worse than this house on 104th Street. It does not seem possible, but after the house Momma described on the Lower East Side where M.S. is living, the investigators are probably telling the truth.

Momma has to decide where she wants to live and then each Saturday and Sunday we will help her walk the streets looking for vacancy signs. It is possible that Charles will come home before the police get to him first, if he can have his own room.

Momma and Edgar can sleep in one room, Harriet and myself can share a room and Charles should have his own room. That means we need three bedrooms unless we use the living room as a bedroom. We also need a kitchen and a separate bathroom and toilet. We must have white curtains and a wool rug instead of linoleum. And in my room there will be a desk and bookshelves on the wall. We must decide whether we want to stay in Manhattan or go to Brooklyn, the Bronx or even Queens.

We are not prisoners here. No one is forcing us to stay in this building. We can leave at a moments notice. We have no lease. We pay our rent from check to check.

I hope Momma has not fallen into that trap where she thinks she has to stay in this building because she has to be punished. If that is so then we may never move. That would be impossible to. Nobody could stay here forever except for the old people who can barely get out of their beds and who already look dead.

We had a talk with Momma tonight. Harriet and me. Momma said we should think of moving to Brooklyn because the Bronx is bad. She said we would go out this Saturday and look at houses in Brooklyn.

In bed, Harriet said, Do you think Momma means it?

I didn't answer Harriet. Momma was so gentle with M.S. Yet she has permitted all of us to live in this building for over a year. I don't know what to think. Is Momma what they call in the newspapers a welfare mother? What is a welfare mother? If I had to describe Momma now, I would say she is somebody who has had children she didn't want to have and she feels taking care of them is a punishment even if she seems to care for us. Momma knows she can never give us the things other mothers can give. She can never demonstrate her love and this keeps her away from us. Momma almost never talks to us. We never have discussions at dinner. Momma doesn't know what I am doing in school. She doesn't know that I am the best reader in our class. She doesnt know that I get the highest grades in math. She doesnt know that I get the best grades in science. She doesnt know that I read four grades above my level and that I am three grades above my level in math. She doesn't know that I want to go to college and that it is possible to go to college if your grades are high enough. She doesnt know that I want to be a lawyer. But what will happen if some man grabs me in the hall or in this room and forces me to have a baby? I can see Edgars father looking at me. He has already put his hands on me, which I took away. For three girls in this building that is just the way it happened.

February 27

On Saturday Momma said her stomach hurt her. She was in bed all day.

March 3

There has been no news from Charles. Harriet thought she saw Charles on 103rd Street.

March 5

M.S.'s investigator came to the door to tell Momma that M.S. left her children in the room on the Lower East Side and is gone.

March 7

Harriet told me that she has a new boyfriend. She said he is not like R., always wanting to be in bed. I asked Harriet what makes this boy different. She said, He talks to me a lot. I asked Harriet if he was on welfare. Harriet said she didn't know any one who was not on welfare.

March 9

I met Harriet and her boyfriend on the sidewalk on 103rd Street. He is tall and looks older than 14. All the boys look old.

March 11

Harriet won't come to the library with me. She says only old men sit there.

March 12

The test marks arrived today in the mail. It is the first mail I ever received in my life in my name. I received 583 points out of 800 points on the PSAT test that I took in December. Miss A. said it was an excellent mark. The principal called me in to congratulate me. The college adviser called me in to say there was no question about my ability to do college work. Momma said I'm learning the right things instead of all the wrong things, which she said must take the same amount of learning.

March 14

Charles is almost never mentioned in the house. It is as though he has gone to the corner for a container of milk and is waiting in a long line.

March 15

When I came home from school Momma wasn't home, neither was Edgar. I hate being in the room alone. There was a knock on the door and I wasn't going to answer it but then I thought that if it was a junkie he would break in the door. I answered the knock. It was Edgars father. He said, Where's your mother? I said I didn't know. He sat down at the table. He took a bottle of wine from his pocket and put it on the table. He asked me for a glass. He poured a glass of wine and asked me if I wanted any. I sat on the edge of the bed for a minute, then I said I had to go because I made a date to see a girlfriend. He said, You're going because I'm here. I said I had a date to see a girlfriend. He said, What about a boyfriend, did you ever get it yet, I bet you get it ten times a day. I said I had to go. He said, Not before I give it to you. I said he shouldnt say that to me. He said, Youre just about at the age when your mother started having her babies. I said I had to go. He said, Whats wrong with having a baby now, you can go on welfare and forget everything else? I said I had to go. He said I needed a baby, then the room wouldnt be so crowded, I could get my own room. He said he was thinking of moving in with Momma when she gets a little more room. I said I had to go. He said, I'm going to give it to you. I started walking toward the door. He didn't reach out to stop me. He said, Next time, I was just getting you ready for next time.

My legs were like water in the hallway. I held on to the railing going down the stairs. The air was dirty and polluted outside but it felt good to be outside. I walked to the corner and went into the park. It didn't seem possible that the trees grew right at the edge of the sidewalk. But they do and they are tall and beautiful.

Should I tell Momma what Edgars father said or shouldn't I? I decided not to say anything. He looked drunk and maybe he wanted to make himself feel like a man when he saw me alone in the room. He is not a man. He lives like an animal. Momma says she uses him like an animal, which is true. About 5 times a month he is in bed with Momma. I don't know why Momma can't find a better man. But where can she meet a man? She doesn't belong to a church. She belongs to no social organizations. She goes to no meetings. She lives here in this room. She never has a chance to meet a man. I think that is why she holds on to Edgars father. He is a habit. There are some organizations that Momma can join like the Parent Association at school. Maybe if more Mommas spoke up at school there could be a change for the best. About 20 kids in my class are reading three or more grade levels below what they are supposed.

Some can't read at all. It doesnt seem possible that in my class there are children who can't read a simple 1st grade book. The teachers stare past these children. They never see them. Most of the teachers go on pretending that they are teaching. It must be horrible for the teachers who have so much responsibility with the life of the children they teach. What a teacher does has no end, it goes on for the life of the child, for all eternity, the teachers teach a child what he will know for the rest of life. If the teachers run away, who is there to stay behind?

One day Mommas like Momma will have to come out of their fear that they have no voice, no brains, that they have to be silent and afraid because they are getting welfare.

Is Edgars father what is waiting for me? He will never get me on the bed. He will never open my legs. I will fight him every minute. I will keep a bottle opener by the side of the bed. I will rip the bottle opener across his neck if he comes near me. I will have a bottle opener by the wall. He will never be able to get past my crossed legs. I will scream and scream. I will never have a baby by Edgars father. That can't be permitted to happen. But it has happened in this building and more than once.

I stayed in the park only a few minutes. Just to believe it was there. I crossed Central Park West. When I got to the house, the stoop was filled with men sitting on the steps. They were drinking from two bottles, passing the bottles around. Some of them I know had TB and other diseases, that's why they were on welfare. The men sit and drink all day. The doctors must have a pill other than wine for these men.

The men on the stoop didn't say anything to me. These are not the dangerous men. These are the sick men. The dangerous men are the fathers like Edgars who come around after dark, who fill the building with arguments, who fight and scream and who fill the women with babies. These men belong to no one. When they steal or take money from the mothers it becomes worse. The mothers scream. The fathers tell the mothers they can go to welfare and say their money was stolen or their money was taken from them. They see welfare as a big pile of money. They are mad because they cannot get more money from the pile of welfare money. They would take all the money they can. Some of the fathers do take all of the money and they tell the mothers to go on the street. There is no way of punishing these fathers. I think they are beyond punishment. They have produced human life. This ought to have some meaning. But it doesn't. A life doesn't have meaning until other persons see you as human, until other persons give you love, feel you are alive. That is why this building is so terrible for all of us, there is no love.

March 18

Momma actually went to Brooklyn. She didn't say anything to us except she didn't see any place worth moving into. Isn't there any place in Brooklyn better than this place?

March 22

My history teacher asked me today if I expected to go to college. I said, I am going to college.

I went to the library on 100th Street after school today. Miss C. smiled at me when I came in. I borrowed 5 books today. There are some books I can't wait to read. I started *The Little Prince* in the library. There is so much light and air in the book. I sat at the corner table I like and opened the book as though it was a special privilege. A writer shares with you what he knows, Miss A. said in class. Writing must be harder than anything else, even if everybody can write or should be able to write. Harriet says she hates writing. When she has to write something for school she never writes more than two sentences and she never uses periods. Why should I write what the teacher knows? Harriet said to me. Why does a writer write a book? Writing is like praying you speak to some one you can't see, will never see, will never know but yet you know they are listening through reading, you hope they are listening, you want them to listen. I can't imagine that a writer only writes for himself. The first pages of *The Little Prince* told me it was written for me. I read until 7:30, then I talked to Miss C. for a while and left with 5 books. I wish I had a room just to read, in a house like they show in the old books with children wearing long black stockings and curled up on a bench by a window with a soft summer light coming in through the window on the pages of the book. Do such houses still exist? They must. I love the library but I would love a house more.

I remember the lady investigator who tried to tell Momma that she should look for a house in Queens. The lady investigator told Momma that some people were giving up their houses in Queens and they were for rent for about the same rent we were paying for one room on 104th Street. The investigator almost begged Momma to go to Jamaica in Queens to the streets where there were real houses. The investigator made the houses seem big, comfortable, safe. The investigator kept telling Momma welfare can give you a lot of money for rent, it can give you more money for rent than you can get for food or clothing or anything else. Momma flatly said, welfare has never given me anything it didn't take back a thousand times.

March 26

Two boys were arrested in the playground for selling drugs. One of them used to live in this building. Is this the way we will find out where Charles is?

March 27

Harriet asked me in bed if you took drugs once did it mean you had to go on taking them for the rest of your life?

I asked Harriet if she had taken drugs. She said no. But she said *no* in a way that meant yes.

March 28

Harriet talking about drugs made me realize something that I have been afraid to think about even to myself. The sight of all the children in my school and on the street who look sick. Not just sick in the body but in their mind. Their eyes seem dull, empty. They almost never talk. They don't play in the games. They stand off. They sit in class in their seats as though they are trying to hide from the teacher. They don't have to bother. The teachers never notice them. This is what M.S.s children looked like upstairs. They were naked in the room, crawling on the floor and none of them looked human. They looked at me as though I was some kind of an object and not a human person. Will that dull empty unhuman look in their eyes stay with them for the rest of their lives?

March 29

Harriet has taken drugs. More than once. I see the scars on her arm.

April 1

The city housing authority sent Momma a telegram saying they were holding a five room apartment for her. April Fool.

April 5

I have to know whether to tell Momma about Harriet.

April 8

Maybe Harriet hasn't really taken drugs in her arm. It doesn't seem possible.

April 9

Momma went out today with Edgar. She took him to St. Lukes Clinic. His asthma is getting worse. He chokes and it seems like he is dying.

Harriet and myself were alone in the room. I asked Harriet to show me her arm. I said, Are these from a needle? Harriet said yes. I said, Where did you take the drugs? Harriet said, In an apartment on 103rd Street. Whose? I asked Harriet. A girl in my class. Where did she get it from? I asked Harriet.

Harriet said, She got it from a boy on 102nd Street.

Did they force you to take it? I asked Harriet.

Harriet said, No.

Then why did you take it? I said.

It didn't seem like anything wrong, Harriet said.

Was it wrong after you took it?

No, it just seemed like nothing. I didn't feel anything. I don't know why everybody gets excited. Its more trouble to take than anything else.

But it can hurt you, I said to Harriet.

More than what? she said.

Then why do you take it?

Maybe because I'm not supposed to, Harriet said.

Were you sick from it?

No. I'm just sick all of the time now. It doesn't make any difference whether its day or night, I feel sick. I feel sick in a heavy way. I can feel the sickness, Harriet said. My head just keeps saying, youre sick, youre sick, I wish I had myself a baby now, then I would be too busy to be sick all the time.

Do you want me to tell Momma? I asked Harriet.

She would kill me.

Then what are you going to do, keep taking the drugs? I asked Harriet. Maybe I won't, Harriet said. The ones who take it dont seem like theyre really getting something. Its no fun to be with them. They are so serious about nothing. They treat the needle and the drug like it is some kind of god. They dont talk about anything else. They just sit around and look at each other. Theres no fun between them. They never laugh.

They never go anyplace. Just to steal if there is no money. In S.s room there was a new TV set, 5 transistor radios, 2 Polaroid cameras, a suitcase, 6 mens suits, a fur coat.

Did you steal anything yet? I asked Harriet.

Just from the A&P when they said they were hungry. Nobody had money so they said I should steal three cans of tuna from the A&P.

What if you got caught?

They told me the manager of that A&P is soft on kids who steal food. He thinks its for the family.

I can't tell Momma anything right now. She would go screaming into the hallways and beat Harriet so that she couldnt go anyplace. If Harriet shows any signs of getting worse, then I'll have to tell Momma. There must be places to help Harriet. Or would they just send her away to a state hospital or institution?

Momma says she would kill all of the drug pushers. She says the people in the buildings should drag the pushers into the street and tear their bodies to pieces. Momma says the pushers around the schools should be put to death immediately, inside of the playgrounds, she says the children should see the dead bodies of the pushers on the playground cement. She says that is the only thing to do to pushers, there is no law to hold them back, no real law to punish them the way they should be punished for getting children to take drugs. Momma says the children then might see that the pushers are no good and drugs no good. Momma hears Charles is selling drugs. Would she want his body torn to pieces?

If it is so terrible to take drugs, then why doesn't the city swoop down on the drug sellers the way it would swoop down on people who would throw their garbage on the subway tracks?

But this is not the way we think.

April 15

The landlord was robbed of $50 today. We heard that he begged the robber not to kill him. The robber held a knife at his throat for about five minutes. The landlord was shaking. He said he is going to sell this house. Who would buy it? Maybe the city will buy it and tear it down to the ground.

April 17

For the first time we have a super. The landlord hired a big six foot man to look after the building. He takes the garbage out of the hallways. He yells at the people who throw garbage out of their windows. He tries to keep the drunks away from the stoop. I think the landlord hired him to protect his life. More and more men are coming to this building from Manhattan State Hospital. Who looks after such people?

April 19

I was walking in the rain today on my way home from the library. In front of me I heard one of the Irish ladies from 103rd Street say to another Irish lady, It's such a sweet rain. They didn't mind the rain falling on them. The children of the old Irish ladies have moved away and they remain alone, happy to talk to one another. Maybe this was the rain they used to feel on their faces in Ireland. Momma said, You're wet. Momma didn't see my face. It was shining clean.

April 20

I tried to talk to Momma about Harriet today. But Momma turns cold when I start to talk to her about something in the family. Maybe she doesn't want to hear anymore trouble. I don't blame her. But all families have trouble.

April 22

The investigator came today just as I got home from school. This time I saw her looking at me. I guess she thinks I am old enough to have a baby. What do the investigators do when they get back to their office on 125th Street? Does this investigator sit and think about our family? Does she say to herself that Momma needs some new pots and pans and that we don't have a tea kettle? Momma boils the hot water in a pan. Does she ask if Edgar needs new shoes? Does she make sure that Momma is taking Edgar to the clinic for all of his shots? Does she think if I need a new dress for school or new sneakers? The investigator is so powerful. She controls all of Mommas money and everything that Momma needs in life that costs money. She can do so much for Momma, yet all of the investigators that have come into our house for years and years have done nothing. They look at Momma as though she is a piece of stone. They look at us as though we mean trouble for them. This investigator tries to be nice to Momma but it means nothing to try and be nice. This investigator must help Momma find a new apartment. She must help Harriet get away from the drugs. Maybe I could talk to her about Harriet. Maybe this investigator knows what her job is. Maybe nobody knows what an investigator is supposed to do. In all of the buildings around us there are people on welfare, hundreds and hundreds, thousands of people. Do they all live the way

Momma and us live? From what I see, yes. Then it must be horrible. Yet all of these investigators see what is going on.

Momma has no husband to talk to. Every family I know has no husband to talk to. In the outside world, away from welfare, the mothers all have husbands to talk to about what the family needs, what the children need, but not in welfare. The investigator can't be this kind of husband. Most of them look to frightened and they ask stupid questions and they repeat the old stupid questions over and over again out of fear of finding out some new information that might cause them trouble back at the office.

The investigator asked Momma about Charles.

Momma said she didnt hear from Charles.

The investigator asked Momma about Edgar. Is he healthy?

How can Edgar be healthy when he is almost never in the sun, never in the park, never playing with other boys his age? He just crawls on the floor in this room or lays in bed and he is so grateful when we play and talk to him and when I read him stories. Momma tells him to shut up when he does anything or tries to talk.

The investigator told Momma I was getting good grades in school. Momma said she knew.

The investigator asked Momma if she found an apartment.

Momma said, I wouldnt be living here if I did.

The investigator said, I meant, have you been looking?

Momma said, Where?

Momma and the investigator talked for about 15 minutes. Then the investigator snapped her ballpoint pen, closed her black notebook and was ready to go.

I don't know what the visit means. What was accomplished? Except that the investigator saw with her own eyes that Momma was alive and so she can still get checks.

April 24

I was walking on Broadway and 102nd Street. I heard Charles call my name. He smiled at me when I turned around. Charles was wearing a gray jacket. He looks so young and so old.

Is Momma around? he asked me.

No, I said.

Where you going? he asked me.

Just to get a notebook, I said.

Have you got money? Charles said.

I said I had a quarter.

Charles took some money out of his pocket. He said, Here's a dollar for you and Har.

Where are you staying? I asked.

Charles said, I can't tell you, then Momma would be dragging investigators around to me.

What do you do? I asked Charles.

He said, I cant tell you that.

What can you tell me? I asked Charles.

Nothing, he said.

Why? I said to him.

He said, Everything I do cant be talked about.

Do you have a room? I asked Charles.

I don't sleep in the doorways anymore, if that's what you mean.

You cant have your own room, I said to Charles, youre to young, nobody would rent you a room.

I stay with somebody.

Who?

I cant tell you that, Charles said.

Is it that white man? I asked him.

Its another white man, Charles said.

What kind of a white man? I asked.

He works in a restaurant downtown.

Why do you stay with a white man?

We get along.

Doesn't he know you should be in school?

I told you theres nothing I do that we can talk about, Charles said.

What do you do? I asked Charles.

I steal a little, Charles said.

What about the drugs?

That to.

Harriet took some, I said.

Charles stopped on the sidewalk. He looked at me and asked, You to?

I said no.

Charles asked me how long Harriet has been using it.

I said, A couple of times.

That's what she says, it must be more.

How do you stop it? I asked Charles.

I dont know, Charles said. Nobody knows. A lot of kids just stop. They don't need it. It doesn't do anything for them.

Do you still use it?

Not like before. I got other things working.

Should I tell Momma I saw you?

It doesn't matter.

Why wont you come home? I asked Charles.

I'd only be there a couple of minutes. Then I'd be locked up and in court. I know a lot of kids who have been that route now, Charles said. If they catch me all right but if they dont catch me, I'll stay away. The court and the lock up stinks.

I didn't believe I was walking with my 12 year old brother on Broadway talking about such things. But we were. It made the entire street look strange, like it was all made out of broken glass and steaming tar and the people were all laughing at us without the laughter being heard.

Charles looked so strange. He looked like any other boy on the sidewalk but he walked like a man. There was no more being a boy for Charles, he would never have the childhood of a boy, he would never build airplane models, join the Boy Scouts, go to camp, play baseball, go swimming, all that was gone for him. He was a man now. He was a man in the body of a boy. That was all I could see. I could not imagine him back in the room sleeping between me and Harriet, running to the grocery store on 104th Street for Pepsi-Cola, staying always in the corner of the room watching the TV set as though he was nailed to it. I know why he would watch so much television. Every program had an ending, a criminal was caught, a problem solved, it was all complete, and so he didn't have to do anything but watch to feel that everything would be solved for him. But the minute he got away from the TV set everything was mixed up. Charles never once in his life spoke to a man who was his father. What this means I don't know, but it must mean as much to Charles as it does to me.

Charles and myself walked along Broadway to 96th Street. It was so strange the way he acted like an older brother, it was as though he was showing me Broadway for the first time. At 92nd Street, Charles said he had to go. Go where? Where does he go? What is his day like? When does he decide to steal? Where does he steal? What does he steal? What does he talk about with the white man in the room? Who makes him breakfast? Who washes his clothes? Who sees to it that his teeth are brushed?

Charles and myself have different fathers. We all have different fathers in our family. Maybe that is why we are not so close to each other. Why we all seem to live apart. As though there is no link. But Momma should be a link.

Momma should watch us like a tiger.

Charles said, I'll see you.

I said to Charles, Cant you tell me where to find you if I need to find you?

Charles said, There's no reason for you to need to find me. I hear a lot of the news from 104th Street.

April 25

Edgar had to stay in St. Lukes Hospital because of his asthma. Momma goes to see him every day.

April 27

Edgar is home. But he will have asthma for the rest of his life.

May 3

Edgar's father spent the night with Momma. He pulled the bedsheets off. He and Momma were naked. When he saw me looking at them, Edgar's father pointed a finger at me, meaning I'm next. Harriet was excited by them and couldnt sleep.

Momma was moaning a lot and kept saying, We have to have our own room. Edgar's father said, Shut up and pay attention to what youre doing.

May 10

The new super throws out a lot of garbage from the halls but the halls still smell.

May 16

Edgars father grabbed me today in the hallway. The new super saw us and he looked funny at Edgars father. Edgars father tried to joke. The new super just stared at him. He asked Edgar if he was registered in Mommas room. Edgars father said, No, he said he comes to visit his boy, Edgar. The new super said, Like s. you do, and walked away.

May 20

Momma asked me if Edgars father has been bothering me. I said yes. Momma asked if he did anything to me. I said no. She said, Did he get you into bed? I said no. Did he try, Momma asked. I said yes.

May 23

There was a pounding on the door. Edgars father said, Let me in. Momma said nothing. Edgars father pounded on the door again. We heard the new super. He asked Edgars father what the hell he wanted and why he was waking people up? He told Edgars father to get out of the building or else he would throw him down the stairs. It seems so strange for there to be any kind of decency in this building.

May 25

Momma went to court to get a court order against Edgars father. She can show her warrant to a policeman and have Edgars father arrested if he bothers us.

May 28

Edgars father and the new super had a fight. They fought in the middle of 104th Street. They were fighting with their hands when Edgars father picked up a pipe that was laying in the street. He started beating the new super over the head with the pipe. The men from the stoop tried to stop Edgars father. The new super fell to his knees and Edgars father was still beating him. The new super was stretched out on the street with blood rushing out of his head. The men on the stoop didn't know what to do. The landlord called for an ambulance. A police car came to a stop in front of the building. The policemen rushed to the new super. Edgars father was still holding the pipe. The police put handcuffs on him. The police said the new super was still alive. I felt good when I heard it. I didn't want Edgar to have a father who was a murderer. I didn't want the new super to die. No matter how bad the building was, he seemed to make it a little better.

I looked up at the windows in the buildings on 104th Street. Most of the windows were open with people looking down on the police and the ambulance. Maybe I am wrong and I hope I am, but everybody staring down on the bleeding super and the police seemed to be enjoying themself. They were getting pleasure from the sight of the super and the whirling red lights. This is what I am most afraid of. That this life in the building on 104th Street is not seen as bad. As something to be ashamed of. The worse the life becomes, the more Momma seems unwilling to move or make any changes. I see this in the faces of the other people in the building. They enjoy their failure. Like the children in class who boast about getting 30 and 40 on tests. I don't know what this means, but somebody must know. There is nobody here to make you want to do things better. I said to Momma that the mothers on the street should take their brooms and sweep down the sidewalk and the street, then maybe the drunks and junkies and everybody else wouldn't leave the sidewalks so dirty. I said that maybe the children should do it after school to. Momma said, There is a city department of sanitation to keep the sidewalk clean. There is an answer for every argument and so nothing gets done. The new super didn't die. The ambulance took him to St. Lukes. I don't know what we would do without St. Lukes Hospital.

June 3

The school year will soon be over. It doesn't seem possible. The teachers complain about the trouble at school but they do nothing. Everyone will pass again. Even those who still can't read or write.

June 5

The heat has become unbearable in our room. I'm fighting now with Momma. Tonight Momma told me to get pregnant and get my own welfare checks if I wanted to get out of the house so bad.

June 7

Harriet told me tonight in bed that she got $5 from Mr. D. on the 3rd floor. She said she needed the money to pay for her share of the drugs. She said the girls told her this is the easiest way to get money.

June 8

I can't tell Momma about Harriet. Momma would just kill Harriet with her bare hands. Momma went to the jail to see Edgars father. The new super is still in the hospital. If he dies, Edgars father will be a murderer.

June 10

The new super died. Edgars father is a murderer.

June 15

The police came to talk to Momma. They looked at the room with disgust. They asked if Edgars father had been contributing to the support of Edgar. Momma said no. They said, Son of a bitch. They asked Momma a lot of questions. Nobody knows how the fight started between the new super and Edgars father. This is what the police wanted to find out. The police kept staring at me but they didn't ask me any questions. Harriet wasn't home. Maybe the police would have noticed that Harriet is taking drugs. I can't tell anybody about Harriet because I don't know what they will do to her. I don't want to be the one to lock up Harriet. She will come out worse from a lock up. That is what everyone says at school who knows somebody who has been locked up.

The police couldn't find out from Momma how the fight started.

June 18

With the new super dead, the garbage is piling up in the hallways again. I saw the landlord carrying down some bags of garbage. His face looked red, as though he was going to faint. His wife was behind the chicken wire yelling, The pigs, the pigs. When she saw me, she said, Not you darling.

June 22

The investigator came and said, I heard there was a murder.

Momma said yes.

The investigator said, Now we know where Edgar's father is.

Momma said yes.

You knew all the time where he was, the investigator said.

Momma said, He would come here but I never knew where he lived or what he did, he would never tell me.

The investigator said, Why did he kill the super?

Momma said, They had a fight and he began hitting him with a pipe. That's all anybody knows.

The investigator said, Does this convince you to move?

Momma said, This wasn't the first killing on 104th Street.

What will convince you to move? the investigator said.

Momma said, An apartment better than this room.

Have you seen Charles? the investigator asked.

No, Momma said.

What about moving across the street? the investigator asked.

Momma said, Those apartments have two rooms but they are twice as worse as this room.

You're right, the investigator said.

This is the way Momma and the investigator talk. The investigator crosses her legs and her nylon stockings don't have any rips. She smokes all of the time. When she leaves the room is filled with smoke. She writes almost nothing in her black book. She tries to talk to Momma like a friend. But it doesn't work. How can she and Momma be friends? Or talk like friends? Momma asked the investigator for money to buy a stroller for Edgar. The investigator said she would take care of it.

Whatever Momma needs, the investigator has to take care of it. It must make Momma feel terrible. But Momma has no choice unless by some kind of miracle she can get out of this building, out of welfare and have her own money. This means Momma would have to work or else get married. Momma never had a chance to work. Working might have made all of the difference for Momma. I don't think she would live this way if she had worked before having her babies. She would have had her own money. She would have been part of more of a world than she is now. She might even be thinking of working now. We can look after Edgar. Whatever money Momma would make working would probably be more than she gets on welfare.

June 23

I saw the Statue of Liberty today. It should be moved from the water that surrounds it and placed on Broadway and 96th Street where everybody can see it. Miss A. said the people who see the statue today are tourists and not like the immigrants who wept when they saw the torch in the sky.

Miss A. said in class that we should see the statue because it is history. Today she took our class. We went by subway. Not like the immigrants who came by boats. When we got out of the subway I could smell the sea air. Miss A. said Europe was 3000 miles away. Miss A. said there is more water than land in our world. Some great power in the heavens should dip this island underneath the sea water and wash it clean.

Miss A. wore a white blouse and a blue skirt. She had a red silk scarf with five-pointed blue stars. Miss A. started to tell us that when she was a girl she had her own sailboat and she would sail out of New Rochelle into the Long Island Sound. But then she stopped suddenly. I thought I saw a blush on her face. But it ended when she said, Theres the Statue of Liberty boat.

I stood in the front of the boat.

We passed tugboats and freighters in the harbor. Miss A. said, This is luck, there's the *Queen Elizabeth*. It was black and white and red. The *Queen Elizabeth* came straight toward us, going to Europe. It gave loud blasts. The air shook. She moved like a queen.

Were you ever in Europe? I asked Miss A.

On that boat, Miss A. said.

I could see Miss A. in the great dining room of the *Queen Elizabeth*. Seated at a table with stiff white napkins. I used to love walking the decks, Miss A. said to me. In the morning before the sunrise its beautiful, Miss A. said.

Were you ever frightened on the ocean? I asked Miss A.

Yes, she said, in the middle of the Atlantic when I suddenly realized that water was lapping against my porthole and only water was around me. I wondered what I was doing in the middle of the ocean and how I would ever get to a shore again if anything happened to the ship.

I feel that way on land.

It was a voyage going toward the statue. From the land it looked close. On the water it was distant. The statue looked familiar even if I had never seen it before. But as the boat got closer and closer, as the statue stood up the way Momma sometimes stands up to make herself look 10 feet tall when she wants to tell us something she doesn't want us to forget, then the statue didn't look familiar. It was bigger than anything I had ever expected. It was a wonder of the world. In more ways than one.

We docked on Liberty Island.

I stretched my neck up to see the statue from the ground. Miss A. said we could take an elevator up to the base of the statue and we could walk to the top. Miss A. said there were 168 steps. The steps were steeper than the steps on 104th Street. But when we got to the top it was worth it, unlike the climb on 104th Street.

I stood in the head of the statue. In front of me was my home. Was this really my home? Those buildings sticking up into the air. They were as thick as the pages in the telephone book. But the water and the sky was beautiful, and the bridges. One bridge looked like a fortress out of the middle ages. Miss A. said it was the Brooklyn Bridge. Miss A. puffed a little on the climb.

Way off we could see the Empire State Building where King Kong fought off the airplanes. I would like to see Momma climb out on to the torch of the Statue of Liberty and stand there in the sky and light fighting off 104th Street.

Miss A. showed us in class an old picture of immigrants coming into New York harbor. The immigrants had all rushed to the side of the ship that was passing the Statue of Liberty and the ship looked like it was going to topple over. They came for freedom. They believed in freedom. Freedom was something they could touch and feel. The Statue of Liberty was freedom for them. Was it freedom for all of them? Freedom is such a beautiful word. It doesn't need an explanation. It is one of those words that makes the rest of the words we use seem so right and true.

Miss A. showed us the famous poem. There I felt I was standing in the middle of history. How right and true the poem reads. I read it to myself. But it seemed like a 1000 voices were reading it with me. Flocks of sea gulls could carry the poem to 104th Street.

I will never forget that statue standing on a little island in the middle of the water. It should move closer to the city now. Maybe in the middle of one night soon the statue will get down from its pedestal and walk through all of the streets of this city.

Miss A. asked me how I liked the statue.

I said I wished more people could see it.

June 24

Harriet came in at 11:30 and Momma started beating her. In bed later Harriet whispered to me that she made $10 tonight.

June 28

The police came to tell Momma that the new super died of a heart attack and not from the iron pipe. Edgars father is not a murderer.

July 3

The end of school again. I wonder when school will really begin. Today in the library I was in the middle of stacks looking for books to read. The books were like knights all around me, ready to protect me when I needed them. I can tell by the feel of a book if I will like it. I can tell by the lines on the first page, if the author speaks to me. It is so good to feel lost in the stack of books. It is so good to reach up, to pick out a book, to look through it and then put it back on the stack if I feel the book is not what I want to read. It is my time that I spend with a book. When I read, it is as though I am writing the book as I read it. These are the books I love to read, the books that make me feel I have written them. This is the way I felt about *The Red Pony*.

The library is clean. The library on 100th Street is old but it is also clean. Miss C. told me that a new library would be going up soon. Tonight Miss C. said I might like *Wuthering Heights*. I looked for it in the stacks but it was out. I put in a reserve. In the library I am me.

July 8

The heat is terrible in the room. Edgar keeps crying. He is big enough now to knock things over and Momma keeps hitting him. Momma keeps turning her face away from Harriet. She doesn't want to see what is happening to Harriet. Momma and Harriet never talk. Harriet is never in the room. Only to sleep at night. Momma sometimes says to her, Where are you going? Harriet only says, Out. Harriet wears a sweater now even in the warm weather to hide her arms. She is never without a covering on her arms. Harriet still takes drugs. She says she meets every day with the girls she sees and they all take it. Why can't they take another kind of drug? But the heroin they take is like this building, a habit. Harriet now has the habit of this building which is to make you feel that you can never live any place else. Today I asked Momma again about moving and she didn't answer me.

July 10

Edgars father is out of jail. Everybody looks at him like he is a murderer.

July 27

I couldn't sleep. I fought back choking. I don't want to suffer from asthma. It was three A.M. No wonder the neighbors are always telephoning the police. I could hear screams and shouts. Somebody called out from a window, Shut up you son of a bitches or I'll start shooting. There was no gun fire. The shouts and screams went on. All the people can do on 104th Street is hurt one another. I listened to the shouts and screams until I fell asleep.

When I woke up Momma was sitting at the table drinking coffee. Edgar was sleeping on the floor. Harriet wasn't in bed. I thought Harriet had run away. But Momma said she went down for milk.

I washed at the sink. Momma seemed to be waiting for me to sit down. I always have cornflakes in the morning.

Momma looked as cold as stone. I didn't say anything. I looked at my cornflakes and couldn't eat.

Momma said, Why don't you eat? I said, I'm not hungry.

I was wet from the heat. Momma was smoking a cigarette. Momma was wearing a robe that Harriet and myself bought her two years ago at Johns.

The landlord is going to show us an apartment across the street, do you want to come and see it? Momma asked me.

Is it one of the two room apartments? I asked Momma.

Yes, she said.

In the front or back?

The back, Momma said.

Is the rent $30 a week?

Yes, Momma said.

Can't we move into a nice apartment for $30 a week? I said, that's a lot of money which very few people can afford for rent.

There's nothing else to see, Momma said.

Momma took off her robe and put on a cotton dress. Momma is getting fat. I never see her eat anything but bread.

The landlady told us, This is a nice apartment. You'll enjoy living here. She said this on the stoop. I think the landlady is unable to see how ugly her building is.

We went across 104th Street. The landlady opened the door for us. The landlady said, Its on the fourth floor, don't hurry up the stairs, its to hot. The walls were dirty. Some of the steps were broken. The lighted bulbs barely lit the hallways. The smell of frying sausages almost made me sick. The doors had writing on them. The walls were scribbled with words. The landlady said, It cost a fortune to put in kitchens and toilets in all these apartments. Its furnished, the landlady said, but the welfare people will still give you some extra furniture if you need it. We were on the third floor. Momma was sweating. How could she take Edgar down four flights of stairs? The stairway seemed steeper as we got toward the fourth floor.

The door to the apartment was stuck. The landlady played with the key. She said under her breath, They break everything, locks, keys, toilets, sinks, stoves, refrigerators, they break everything and they don't deserve what they get.

The key turned in the lock.

The door opened right into the toilet, the door going past the open toilet and stopping. The kitchen stove was covered with dirt. Some of it fell from the cracked ceiling. The furniture in the living room was a torn studio bed, a broken chair, a torn arm chair. The bedroom had one single bed. The mattress had no sheet on it and the mattress was soiled. The window in the back room was broken. The walls were streaked with crayon. That was the entire apartment.

Its empty now, the landlady said, tomorrow it wont be. The landlady was right. The welfare people would send over a tenant as soon as they got a call from the landlady.

Who lived here? Momma said, was it Mrs. E.S.?

Yes, the landlady said.

Mrs. E.S. was in the Womens Home of Detention. They said she would be there a long time. She was taking some money from a man who was sleeping in her room and he woke up and stopped her. Mrs. E.S. hit him over the head with a butcher cleaver. Her six children were placed by welfare. This happened two days ago.

Momma said, Doesn't anybody fix this place up?

The landlady said, You can fix it up all you like.

Momma said, The walls are broken.

The landlady said, I didn't break them.

Momma said, Dont you have anybody who fixes up an apartment when somebody moves out?

The landlady said, The bed doesn't have time to get cold.

Momma said, I'll look for something else.

The landlady said, Its your privilege, but this will be gone tomorrow.

The apartment *was* gone in the morning. I saw a Puerto Rican lady with 7 babies walk in with the landlady. She only had two suitcases. Where will all of the babies sleep?

We might have been able to clean up the two rooms. But Momma doesn't want to move from our room.

Our room looked small when we got back. It looked dirty. I try to keep it clean but the clothes pile up, Edgar spills the cornflakes on the floor. If Momma won't move, then we must find a way of forcing her to move.

July 30

I have a plan. I will try to see Mommas investigator alone and tell her why it is so important for the investigator to find Momma an apartment through the welfare housing person.

August 2

I telephoned the welfare office. The investigator said she cannot talk to me alone.

August 5

I saw Harriet in the school playground. She looked like a little girl from a distance. But the girls she was with all take drugs.

August 8

Charles waved to me from across the street on Broadway and 101st Street. But he didn't stop to talk.

August 12

The police raided the school playground on 93rd Street but Harriet was getting something for Momma from the A&P at the time.

August 14

Momma heard from an investigator that M.S. is in a state hospital. She never went to pick up her boy at the Childrens Center.

August 19

I didn't go to camp this year. I thought every day we might move.

August 25

Edgars father tried to see Momma. But Momma wouldnt open the door.

August 27

The investigator came today. She pretended not to notice me because of the phone call I made to her. The investigator told Momma that Edgars father refused to sign a paper stating that he was the father of Edgar. The investigator said there would have to be a court hearing and the judge would say who is the father of Edgar. How can the judge tell if Edgars father *is* the father of Edgar? Momma said she didn't want to see Edgars father again. The investigator told Momma that she had no choice, there had to be a paternity hearing downtown. Momma said what I had been thinking, How can the judge tell?

The investigator said she didn't know.

The investigator asked again about Charles.

Momma said she had no word from Charles.

The investigator said she didn't believe a boy 12 years old could live so long alone away from home.

Momma said, Its not what you believe but what's happening. Nobody pays any attention to whats happening, only to what they want to believe.

The investigator didn't like that.

Momma said to the investigator, Are you married?

The investigator said, No.

Momma said, Do you have any children?

The investigator said, No.

Momma said, Do you have a boyfriend?

The investigator said, Not really.

Momma asked, Do you live alone?

The investigator said she shares an apartment.

Momma asked, Does any of this bother you at night when youre trying to sleep?

The investigator said, No.

Momma said, Do you just turn it off?

The investigator said, I dont just turn it off but I dont live with it 24 hours a day either.

Momma said, You should try.

Momma said, Why don't you rent a room here for a week?

The investigator said, I don't have to rent a room here to know whats going on.

Momma said, You don't know whats going on.

The investigator said, I know the toilets are broken, the bathtubs are stopped up, theres garbage in the hallways.

Momma said, I bet you feel good about all this.

The investigator said, I think we can stop this discussion.

Momma said, Why? You never talk to me about anything real. Don't you want to talk real?

The investigator sat up stiff. I could see on her face that she didn't know if Momma was going to become hysterical like some of the other mothers. I felt good about Momma. She was getting the investigator into a corner.

The investigator stood up. She said, I'll be back when youre quieter.

Momma said, Youre a son of a bitch.

The investigator didn't answer.

The investigator left and I hoped Momma's talking up meant she was going to move.

When the investigator left I realized Momma had been drinking, which is something she never did before. That means that buried deep down in Momma there are still the words and feelings to get us out of this room and out of welfare. But how can the words come up out of Momma so that they have real meaning and so that Momma can do what the words say?

When the investigator left, Momma kept talking about the investigator. Momma said, How can they send that little son of a bitch to tell me what to do with my life? That little bitch doesnt know what it means to go hungry, to be dirty, to have babies at Metropolitan Hospital. She knows nothing. Nothing. Just a lot of words that they drill into her so they can be satisfied. Everything is for them down at that god damn welfare office, nothing is for the people who need real welfare. This is the way its been since the beginning of the world, Momma said. How do I get back into that old world, Momma said, the world where people aren't on welfare, thats the only world to be in in this country. Thats the only world that counts. Welfare counts for nothing. Its nothing. Its being dead for you when you're at one year of life, five years of life, ten years of life, eighty years of life. This welfare is a sickness. Its a disease. Its killing Edgar with asthma. It has Charles fg. rotten white men. I know Harriet is going to wind up climbing walls.

I know about you, Momma said, pointing to me, youre going to fight and fight and fight and if youre lucky maybe you wont have to fight anymore and if youre not lucky youre going to be in a room just like this forgetting everything else. Why doesn't somebody tell us that this is a rotten disease. The money means nothing! We don't see the money, we don't keep the money, we cant touch and feel the money, it all goes to the grocery stores and that son of a bitch of a landlord downstairs who wants everybody to pity him because hes getting rich on our dead bodies. Jesus Christ, Momma said, what could make less sense than all of this, this stinking dirty ugly filthy son of a bitching building that ought to be burned to the ground with the ground covered with salt.

Every word Momma said made sense, but in the morning we were still in the building. Edgar was choking. The milk was sour in the refrigerator because something went wrong and the motor turned off.

August 30

I told Harriet that Momma had a fight with the investigator. Harriet said Momma should have killed her first investigator.

September 2

Momma had me write a note to the investigator saying we all needed school clothes.

September 5

Harriet says that she doesnt want to go back to school. She says sitting in class all day doing nothing makes her nervous. Momma said she'll beat Harriet six ways to Sunday if she doesn't stay in school. Momma still doesnt know about Harriet's arm and the drugs or the men who give her $5 bills.

I know Harriet can read and write. That much she learned in the early grades without any trouble. But how much does she know to get through life? I think Harriet stopped learning after the 5th grade. She has just been sitting in class. I never hear her talk about a teacher. She never talks about a subject. She almost never gets homework. School is nothing to her. A place where she closes her eyes and ears. Why does this happen? Is knowledge frightening? Are we afraid to learn more than we can handle? Is this what Harriet wants, to always be a child even when she is a woman? It must be like that. The women in this building are like little girls. They aren't responsible. They let welfare look after them. One day is like a thousand other days. Theres no ambition. No resistance. Otherwise the women in this building would have gotten together long ago either to burn the building down or force the inspectors to inspect and the landlord to fix. But it doesnt happen.

I am sick of saying Momma should move. Now I think of when *I* should move, to protect myself, because this building and the life in the building is a trap. Two more girls became pregnant on the 5th floor, F.L. and E.O. Both are 14. Both want their own welfare cases. I think Harriet and myself are the only girls left in the building who arent pregnant. Harriet doesnt talk about wanting a baby anymore. I think the drugs have made her afraid of having a baby. How could she take care of a baby. And me? Do I want a baby?

No! I don't mean I never want a baby. Of course I do. But I want a baby like a million other women have babies who aren't on welfare. I was with Momma when she brought Edgar home from Metropolitan Hospital. I waited in the little room where the nurses bring the baby to you to take home. I saw girls just a few years older than me taking home babies. Momma was very nervous. She kept telling me to sit still. When the nurse came with the baby Momma got up. The nurse put the baby (Edgar) in Mommas hands. Momma was now the mother of Edgar and his life was her responsibility. We walked to 96th Street and Momma said, Lets take a taxi.

When we got home there was no one to greet Momma and the new baby. Harriet and Charles were watching TV and almost didn't hear us come in. Momma laid Edgar on the double bed. When the TV program was over Harriet and Charles came to look at Edgar. The investigator was late in sending a check to Momma for a crib and Harriet said, Where is the baby going to sleep? We had rats then on 118th Street. Momma said, I'll find him a place. The check for the crib and the bottles didn't come until two weeks later. Momma swore every day at the investigator and kept calling him till she ran out of dimes.

I like fresh towels hot from the laundermat. I like clean stiff sheets. I like a fresh smelling blanket. I like a kitchen table with a white top. I like a bed that you sleep in as though it is your friend for life.

September 7

Harriet told me the pusher for her friends was arrested in front of her school. One of the girls became hysterical when she heard about it and she had to be pulled away from the edge of the roof on 103rd Street. She thought she wouldn't be able to get more drugs.

September 9

In class today P. threw a steel tipped dart at our math teacher. The dart missed her by inches. She grabbed hold of the desk and then started vomiting. It was terrible to see the vomit coming out of her mouth. Two of us ran for paper towels. P. ran out of the room.

September 12

I took the Preliminary Scholastic Aptitude Test last year in my junior year. Miss A. and the principal and the college adviser said I should now take the SAT which stands for Scholastic Aptitude Test. This must mean that the preliminaries are over. This is the *real* test. It is three hours long like the other test but the material is harder. In the Civil Service I know you keep taking tests. Momma sometimes says she wishes she had taken a Civil Service test when she left high school. Momma said she would have been up five or six grades now making more money than welfare can ever give her. When Momma cashed her check today she gave me the first $2.50 to pay for the test. If Momma would have taken one test maybe none of this would have ever happened. Is this what life means, that you must take every test that life gives to you?

I wish there was a new test that Momma could take. A test that would end her days in this room. If Momma passed the test and I know she would, then she could do something for the money she gets from the government. Can't they think of such a test in Washington? Does Momma's life *have* to be this way? I will go into the SAT test for Momma. I will sit there for three hours with Momma at my side. I will answer each question for Momma. There is no question in this world I can't answer that way, except why this life here must be the way it is.

September 15

Why can't Momma see how terrible Harriet looks? Her face is almost that of an old woman. I never see Harriet eat anymore. Whatever Momma puts on the table, Harriet pushes away. Momma doesn't ask Harriet why she doesn't eat, she just takes the food away. In bed I asked Harriet if she is still taking drugs. Harriet said yes. I asked how much. Harriet said she uses it every day now. Why? I asked her. Harriet said it was just something she does after school now everyday with the other girls. I asked about the pusher who got arrested, didn't that stop the drugs? Harriet says there is always a new pusher to take the place of an old pusher, she said she can buy drugs just as easy as she can buy a bottle of Pepsi-Cola. What does the drug do for you? I asked Harriet. She said, Nothing. Then why take it? Why stick a needle in yourself every day that might be contaminated? Harriet said she just does it.

Is Harriet an addict like the men on the stoop? Is she an addict like the men I read about in the newspapers? Is she really and truly an addict? Or is she just taking drugs now because other girls are taking it and this is the thing to do, to belong to if you have no other thing or place to belong to.

Isn't this a problem for welfare? Or for Momma? If I didn't feel that Momma would tear Harriet to pieces I would tell Momma about the drugs.

Maybe Harriet should be in an institution. But the girls at school who have been in institutions say they are a nightmare. They say the guards beat you. They say if you're not a lesbian it doesn't matter, the lesbians go after you like a pack of wolves. They say the teachers don't even bother teaching. They say *if* you are a lesbian, if you like to fight guards, you can get along fine. Since I know now that anything can be true, I believe all these stories. They are probably more terrible than the way the girls tell it because many of the things that happen at the institutions that probably don't seem so terrible to them would seem like a nightmare to other people.

Is there a doctor Harriet can go to? Can she go to the school doctor? Or the school nurse? Where in the city does a 14 year old girl addict go? I wish I could nurse Harriet. Maybe if I spent more time with her. We can go to the library together. We can do more shopping together. We can take a bus once in awhile to 34th Street and look at the store windows. It is two years since I have been to Macys. We can go to the movies, if Momma gives us the money or if I get more babysitting jobs.

If Harriet is kept busy she wont have time to use the needle. If someone was interested in her she would be more interested in that person than in the needle. We all need one person, just one person, to make us feel that we are not alone in the world. I think this is the one feeling all people on earth have.

I am aware of my own existence!

But am I aware of the existence of another person who cares about me, in the same way that I am aware of my own existence?

How much does Momma care about me? Whatever it is that Momma cares about me, she doesn't show it. But I know she cares. Otherwise I would run. In a way I have made up my mind to run. Taking the college test next week is part of it. If Momma doesn't find us a new apartment by the end of the year, an apartment in which we can live like a family and not like prisoners of some kind of a dirty war, then I will leave. I will go down the steps of this filthy building, away from the other filthy buildings on this street and like millions of other people have done in the past, I will go forth to make my own way in the world. I will not do what Momma has done and find myself locked into a past that I do not choose to live in. I cannot believe that Momma deliberately chooses this life for herself. But we have been in this filthy building for almost 2 years and as far as I can see, no person, no law, nothing has forced Momma to remain here. Yet what is it that has forced Momma to remain in this building? It is a mystery. I don't think I can solve it. But I can run from the mystery, just as one runs away from the mystery of death. We don't choose to die in order to find out what death is. It is stupid to choose death in order to find out what life may be.

September 20

Miss A. was right. The SAT test *was* harder. I took it today from 9 to 12 o'clock. I was up at 6 o'clock. Momma was up before me. She had the iron out and was ironing a white dress for me. Momma walked with me to the subway station on 104th Street. In the early morning 104th Street looks as though it has been coated with a thick layer of garbage. Momma didn't say much. 104th Street was speaking for us. But Momma told me a little story. Momma said she had a cousin in Cleveland, Ohio. She said her cousin had a very strict father. When her cousin went to work, her father said that she had to give him $10 a week out of her salary for every week that she worked. Momma said her cousin worked for years. Then when her cousin left her father's house to be married, her father gave her back all of the money she had been giving him. He had been putting it in the bank for her. Momma said to me at the subway, I hope I have been able to put away something for you. I kissed Momma. She started to cry. She said, Do good on the test. I was crying myself on the subway but I wiped away the tears the minute the test began.

September 22

The math teacher has quit. It might be better to hire policemen to teach our class, then something might be learned.

September 23

Miss A. took our class to the Museum of Natural History today. Momma gave me fifty cents. She said she remembered going to the museum and there was a stand where you could buy things. Momma said she bought a picture book on sailing ships. I wish Momma would tell me more of what she remembers.

September 25

Momma is crying. Harriet is crying. I am crying. Charles is dead. He died from an overdose of drugs. The police found him on the sidewalk on 94th Street. The police car was cruising down the street. Some people had walked past Charles' body, letting him lay on the sidewalk. The police got out of the car. The police couldn't save him. Little by little now we know what has been happening and what happened to Charles.

He was staying with a 46 year old white man who worked for a restaurant. The white man was homosexual. He was also a drug addict. He used Charles to sell drugs, so that he could get enough money to buy his own drugs. Charles sold the drugs to children in the schools between 110th Street and 72nd Street. Nobody knows why Charles wasn't caught or arrested. The children were stealing from their parents and neighbors to get money to buy the drugs from Charles. Maybe Charles was never caught or arrested because all of the drug-taking and drug-selling was between children and adults were out of it. Or maybe the adults didn't want to admit that the children were stealing to buy drugs or that Charles was selling drugs and so they all closed their eyes, just as the teachers in our classes close their eyes.

Momma did not have to run through 104th Street begging for money to bury Charles. She had a policy on his life for $750. Momma wanted to cremate Charles. But then she decided to put him into the ground.

I don't know how Charles will be able to spend all eternity in the box they put him into. He wanted to run. Momma was screaming at the grave. She screamed curses at everyone who deserved to be cursed.

When I am older and I have enough money, I will have a marble gravestone made for Charles and on it I will have carved into the marble: *Murdered by the City of New York, the State of New York and the United States of America.*

It will not look so nice in the cemetery but it will be true.

October 4

Harriet told me that some of the kids were off the drugs after Charles was found dead. Now they are back again. Harriet too.

October 8

The investigator came today to tell Momma she was sorry about Charles dying. Momma screamed at her to get out of our room.

October 15

More stories are being told about Charles. Everybody who knew him thought he was 16 years old. Nobody believes he was only 12.

October 20

I walked all of the blocks between 96th Street and 72nd Street looking for vacancy signs today.

October 22

Edgars father came by. Momma let him sleep in her bed.

October 28

Harriet told me in bed that a girl in her class had a baby at St. Lukes Hospital and the baby was addicted to drugs when it was born. The doctors were able to take the newborn baby off of drugs but they could do nothing for the 13 year old girl who died.

November 3

The landlord had his name in the newspapers. He was in court with over 400 violations. The democratic club forced the building inspectors to really inspect this building. The judge said everybody in the building should move. But the judge had no more apartments where the people could go than the man in the moon.

November 5

Mr. T.H. on the 5th floor was robbed tonight. Two boys broke into his room and took his TV set. They tied him to the bed and stuck a dirty towel in his mouth. Mr. T.H. was telling everybody in the hallway that the boys could not have been over 12 years old. He said he didn't dare fight them because they held a knife against his heart. The two boys carried the TV set to the roof and went down the stairs of another building.

November 6

While we were eating dinner Momma asked me and Harriet if we were using drugs. Harriet said no. I said no. What would Momma do if she knew Harriet was using drugs? Could she stop her? Could she begin to give Harriet the kind of love she needs in order to stop taking drugs? Would Momma do this? Would she give Harriet the attention of a mother whose baby is in terrible danger? Maybe. But I think Momma would just collapse. I will tell Momma one day soon that Harriet is using drugs. That is my responsibility. I have told myself that I must tell Momma. What Momma can do for Harriet or what she cant do, isn't for me to question.

Momma should know that Harriet is taking drugs. I have told myself that it is nothing to hide anymore. Taking drugs is a sickness like tuberculosis or measles. It must be treated like a sickness. Not like it is now, like something so full of danger that it gives people a thrill to talk about, while preventing them from doing anything real to help the addicts. Nobody can believe the amount of stealing that goes on just on this block. Everybody says it is the addicts who do all the stealing. They need the money to buy the drugs. If you have not been robbed, it just means that you will be robbed. I have not said anything about all of the robberies in our room because it didn't seem to important. But now I feel it is important because the robberies reveal a sickness. This is not robbing like robbing a bank or supermarket.

Harriet went out after dinner. We ate baked beans and frankfurters. Even Edgar is eating frankfurters now.

Momma and myself were alone except for Edgar who was laying in front of the TV set. Momma will talk when Harriet and myself are in the room. But she almost never talks to me alone.

I thought of what I could tell Momma. Harriet is taking drugs. Edgars eyes are dull, they don't shine like a babys eyes that are seeing the world for the first time and who is made to feel this is his world. Edgar is a stranger already in the world. Somehow Momma has made Edgar unalive. Edgar looks like a dry seed, as though he has to be put into water to be made to bloom. There is no bloom around him now. The touch of his hands arent alive. Doesnt Momma want a son who can inherit the earth?

Momma saw me staring at her. Momma said to me, You think we're never going to move.

I said, I think we should move.

Momma said, We'll move.

When, I asked.

I'm getting ready, Momma said.

There is nothing else to believe except the fact that Momma has been staying in this room to punish herself. How can I tell this to Momma? The words coming from me would make no sense.

What does *ready* mean? I asked Momma.

Momma sat down in front of the television set. When she doesn't want to answer me, she walks away as though I had never spoken.

November 7

Miss A. suggested that I take two Achievement tests. One in English. One in History. The Achievement tests will test what I actually know. What about all those students outside West 104th Street, in *real* schools, with books, records, encyclopedias, World Books, Britannicas, in their houses? With fathers who are doctors, lawyers, engineers? Do I know what they know? Will I be tested against them? Not against myself? Miss A. said I can study for these tests. Miss A. said she would help me with the English questions. Vocabulary is more important than anything else, Miss A. said. If the tests include questions from the vocabulary I have heard most of my life I will be even with the World Books and Britannicas.

November 8

Momma said $2.50 for more tests will never make her any poorer.

November 9

The investigator came to tell Momma that she would have to go into court soon to prove Edgars father is the father of Edgar.

November 10

In the library tonight Miss C. the librarian showed me catalogues of colleges from all over the country just like Miss A. did. I sat and read them until 8:30. Each catalogue contains so much knowledge. They are like a thousand libraries. They read like the stories from *The Arabian Nights* where you go from one door into another door and through doors beyond each door and the wonders keep increasing but all you are looking for is your own life. Miss C. said she would give me a letter of recommendation. What kind of letter of recommendation would Momma write for me? I think it would be to sad and beautiful for anyone to read. Momma told me she heard of welfare stopping other children from going on to college. I can't believe that but then why shouldn't I?

Miss A. and the college adviser are helping me with the applications and scholarship forms. I fill out each form as though it is a prayer.

The principal smiled at me today. He patted my head. He said he was sure I would get a good mark on the SAT. I hope he's right. He is also writing letters of recommendation.

November 11

Momma and myself went to 34th Street today to Macys for the first time in two years. I felt like I was leaving a walled city. I think welfare is a wall around people that keeps getting higher and higher until there is no way out. We went by bus. I have a bad habit of staring at people. Sometimes it gets me into trouble when people think I am staring at them to make them angry. I only stare at people to see if we are all human together. Or if there is a special difference that marks us apart. I think we are all human together.

Momma and myself went into Macys. I felt like I was being buried by all of the things I couldn't have. I own two dresses, four underpants, one slip, pink, one pair of shoes, three blouses, two skirts, one pair of sneakers, one pair of red leather shoes, a rain coat, a blue winter coat and a spring jacket. Momma bought Edgar a sweater. Most of the things Edgar owns and wears Momma has bought at the Goodwill.

I looked at the faces of the mothers in Macys. Were some of them on welfare? Maybe. I looked at Mommas face to see if it would change in Macys, to see if her face would begin to reflect like a light, everything in Macys that a person could have if they worked, if they had money. I thought Momma went to Macys to buy Edgar a sweater so that he would love her for it, and not die like Charles alone on a sidewalk.

Momma gave me a dollar and I bought a yellow blouse that was reduced from $2.98 to 98 cents.

Momma didn't talk on the bus ride back to 104th Street. She stared out of the bus window as though everything she saw was a movie. The movies show us everything we can never have.

I said to Momma before we got to 104th Street, Wouldn't it be nice to move before it gets cold? Momma didn't answer me. But I saw her listen.

November 14

Miss A. took me after school today to a Father who would write a letter for me. Miss A. is acting more like my college advisor than the college advisor, even if I don't have her in class this year. The Father was a short, powerful man who looked like a boxer. He has an office in a storefront. He asked me if I knew what the 14th Amendment was to the Constitution. When I said, That no state shall make or enforce laws that deprive any people of life, liberty or property or deny them equal protection of the law, he smiled like the priests sometimes do in the movies. He asked me what book I liked the most. I said I couldn't make a choice since I had not read them all. He asked me if I had ever heard of Thoreau. I said Miss A. lent me a copy of *Walden* which I read. He said he would give me a copy to keep. I asked him if welfare could keep me from going to college. He said if I could go and they tried to stop me, he would fling the officials out into the street. I believed him.

November 15

Harriet told me a boy grabbed her in a hallway on 107th Street and took her up to the roof. She said she didn't know who to complain to about it and so she is trying to forget it happened.

November 16

I found a book in the library with the whole chronological history of the world to study for the History Achievement test.

November 17

The history teacher walked out of class today and shouted that we could all kill one another if we wanted to. What he meant was that he would like to kill all of us but he doesnt dare or doesnt yet know how. I hope I have learned enough history for the test in case he quits the school.

November 22

The cold days are beginning. The days are short. I need to go to the toilet in the evening but I hold in until I get to school in the morning because the toilet is broken again. The landlady screams that the drug addicts break the toilets. She screams that they come in from the street to shoot drugs into their arms in the toilet. She screams that she cant keep everybody out of the building, that people visit one another, people have friends, she screams, not everyone is a drug addict.

I don't believe the landlady. The toilet is broken because she doesnt want to fix it. I sometimes feel I am getting like Momma by doing nothing. If I feel the landlady wont fix the toilet, then I should do something about it, protest or carry a sign in front of the building, get some people together. I have never heard Momma complain about this building except to an investigator. *The most terrible thing to believe is that Momma has stayed here almost two years because she wanted to be here. I know this is true but I dont want it to be true.*

I tried teaching Edgar the alphabet today, the 26 letters that make up the words of all life. Edgar walks around the room almost like a blind person. His face doesnt have the spark of life I see in other babies faces. I look into the mirror to see if my face has it. I think my face is alive. I read three books a week now and I think the reading of books keeps my face alive because of all the people and places I remember and keep tract of as I read. Reading is carrying on a silent conversation with people you never meet otherwise.

Momma looked at me today and said I needed a brassiere. I said we'll have to ask the investigator to send us money for one and that made her screaming mad. Its good to know that Momma still has feeling.

November 29

Harriet had a terrible fight with Momma.

Momma screamed at Harriet, You're going to be like every other pig in this building!

Harriet yelled back at Momma, You're a pig!

Momma slapped Harriet across the mouth. Harriet didn't cry. She ran out of the room this time and didn't come back until about 11:30 at night.

The fight started when Momma asked Harriet to take the garbage downstairs.

Harriet said Momma should throw the garbage out of the window. Momma insisted that Harriet take it down to the cans. Harriet said Momma should throw it in the hallway. Momma said, Are you going to obey me or not?

Harriet said, You can go to hell if you think I care about keeping this building clean. This building stinks. The bed stinks from bedbugs. The whole place stinks!

Momma yelled at Harriet to shut up.

Harriet wouldn't shut up. She told Momma, You can live in this filth, I wont.

Momma said, You'll do what I tell you to do.

Harriet said, You tell me to live in filth and I wont do it.

Momma said, Shut your mouth.

Harriet yelled back at Momma, Move, move, move, move, move! She yelled it louder and louder at Momma, Move, move, move, move!

Edgar started crying.

Momma said, One more word and you get a beating.

Harriet yelled at Momma, Beat me, that's all you think of, that's the only time you know I'm alive!

When Harriet came back into the room she got into bed with me. Her body was trembling. She put her arms around me and got close to me. She couldn't stop shaking. I asked her what was wrong. She said she put something into her arm. I asked her if she felt sick. She said yes. I said, Do you want to go to the emergency at St. Lukes?

I can't go, Harriet said. Then Momma will know I'm on drugs. Maybe it will go away, Harriet said, I hope so, maybe if I just lay still.

What did you put into your arm? I asked Harriet. Junk, she said, junk. I don't want to die like Charles, Harriet said, I don't want to die like Charles did.

In a little while the trembling stopped but her body was cold and wet. Harriet was all twisted up. The room was cold. We both fell asleep.

During the middle of the night Harriet woke me up and said to me, A train is passing over my body.

December 3

Momma must see that Harriet is sick.

December 5

Edgar had another choking fit. I hope I never get asthma. I don't know why I don't have it. Almost everybody I know goes to the asthma clinic at St. Lukes.

December 8

Momma let Edgars father stay the night.

December 10

Momma and the landlady had a fight. The landlady said to Momma, I dont want that bum in the house, he bothers little girls.

December 12

Miss A. told me the principal wanted to see me. There was a big smile on his sweating face. He told me I got 567 out of 800 points on my SAT test. Miss A. said to me in the hallway, I wish everyone in this school would go to college, a new college, a college that doesn't exist now, a new kind of college, a college that would open up all of the closed doors, open them. Why can't we make it happen, why can't it happen, why can't we build new kinds of colleges with all of the billions and billions of dollars that we have?

I didn't want to tell Miss A. that the reason it isn't done is because we don't want to do it. Is there any other reason?

December 14

In the dirty toilet at school today three girls got around me and started saying, Youre going to a welfare college! Welfare going to pay for your books and pencils! Welfare going to pay for your underpants! Welfare going to pay for your toothpaste! What welfare college do you think you're going to! There was hate on their faces. They started to shove me. They picked at my face like crows. D.M. said, See this belly, this the welfare college you're going to. D.M. is pregnant. She is leaving school.

I didn't let them shove me to far. I didn't fight back because they would cut me. I just stood up to them. They are really cursing themselves, not me.

December 15

I go every night now to the library, if I can. I like the walls lined with books. If I ever have my own house it will have books and books. Every room will be filled with books and flowers. Fresh flowers. I would like the sun to come into every room. The kitchen will get the most sunlight. The sunlight in the kitchen will be as bright as the sun. There will be no cracks in the walls. The paint will be clean and fresh, smooth. The floor will be shining. There will be room to sit around the table.

December 17

There is a rumor that the landlady is planning to sell the building.

December 18

The rumor wasn't true.

December 19

In the morning I will take the English Achievement test. It sometimes seems so strange to me that we would have to study so hard to learn our native language. Is it this way with all the people and their native language? I do not know why but I think it is easier for other people. I think they find their native languages easier. Maybe its because our language seems borrowed. The English we speak did not spring from our soil. English is a foreign language for most of us. I think when it becomes our *real* language we will then find it easier to speak to our selves. I have gone over the rules of grammar, vocabulary lists, literature books Miss A. gave me, but what I seem to remember best of all are the cardboard letters of the alphabet Momma put up on the wall for me. They were signposts. I will look for them in the room where I take the Achievement test.

December 20

I would like to die during Christmas and be reborn on the first of the year. I do not believe that we are going to spend another Christmas in this room. How did it happen? Where have the days gone?

December 25

God bless ye merry gentlemen, on this our Christmas Day.

December 27

We didn't give each other presents and none of us seemed to notice. I think it is because Charles is dead and Harriet is dying.

December 30

The investigator came and Edgars fathers hat was hanging on a hook. The investigator couldn't help noticing a mans hat. She said to Momma, Did you hear from the court yet?

Momma said, No.

The investigator said, There will be a trial. When you get the notice you have to go.

Momma said, How can the judge tell who is the father of Edgar?

The investigator said, The judge will ask you and Edgars father a lot of questions. Then he makes a decision.

It's crazy, Momma said.

Nobody said it isn't, the investigator said, but the court hasn't found a better way to determine who a father is. They take a blood test of Edgars father but that will only prove that he *can't* be the father, not that he is the father.

I know, Momma said, who the father is.

Then you tell the judge, the investigator said.

What if the judge doesn't believe me? Momma said.

Then you will still know who is the father of Edgar, even if the court doesn't know, the investigator said.

It is crazy, Momma said.

Who does the hat belong to? the investigator asked Momma.

Jesus, Momma said, Jesus Christ, our Lord.

The investigator didn't like that. She closed her black book. This is a new investigator. She is short, very thin and black. She keeps clicking her ball point pen. She seems to write down almost everything Momma says. She looks at me but she didn't say a word to me.

Who does the hat belong to? the investigator asked again.

Momma said in a very cold and tired voice, Get out of here with those kind of questions before I cut your face to pieces.

The investigator said, Your case could be closed.

Momma said, Just stand up and get out of here. I don't want to see you walk through that door again. You keep looking at that hat like I'm hiding a million dollars somewhere in this stinking room. Get out and don't come back.

The investigator said, Don't you ask me for anything.

Momma said, You don't have anything to give. Youre a black pig.

When the investigator left, Momma went to the sink and poured herself a glass of cold water. She didn't bother to rinse the glass and there was a cockroach swimming on top of the water. Momma threw the glass against the wall. She went to her bed and lay down. She stretched out her body. She didn't say a word to me. She kept looking up at the ceiling. Edgar started crying. Momma kept her hands stiff alongside her body. She didn't move when Edgar started crying.

I walked out of the room, down the dirty steps, down the dirty hallway, past the dirty men on the stoop and when I got to the corner where no one could see I started crying.

January 5

If I run away, where can I run to? If I don't get to college and have to stay with Momma, what will happen to me?

January 7

Harriet thinks she is going to have a baby. She says it might have come from the boy who took her up to the roof on 107th Street.

January 10

I wish I had an aunt in Cleveland, Ohio with a big house and a room for me that I could decorate myself. My only two aunts are on welfare and one lives on West 117th Street, the other one lives on West 112th Street.

January 15

All the tests for college are over now. Why didn't they have questions about West 104th Street on the tests?

January 20

Momma and myself dont say 10 words to each other now during a night.

January 25

The landlady said to me today that I am beginning to look like a young woman. She tried to sell me a dirty green blouse for fifty cents.

January 28

A welfare investigator was dragged into a room on West 103rd Street and raped.

January 29

I needed a father today. Momma told me and Harriet not to be in the room tonight. A new man has been seeing Momma and she obviously wants him in her bed without us watching for a change. It's all right for Edgar to watch. Momma said we should come back at about 11. She gave us money for the movies.

This is the first time this has happened. It means that Momma is now ashamed for us to be in the room while she is having a man in her bed.

What does Momma think we think of all the times she had Edgars father in her bed and we listened to them?

Harriet didn't want to go to the movies. She took me to a candy store where she hangs out at night. The candy store was on Columbus Avenue. It was long and narrow. In front was a counter. In the back were some tables. The entire store was filled so that you had to squeeze your way in. There was a lot of smoke. There was a lot of loud music. Everybody seemed to be yelling. The faces were stiff and frozen. There was no joy in the room. Just a hardness. A terrible hardness, like all of the bodies were ready to crack in half.

Harriet fit right in. I felt I was in a cage. The boys all looked like Charles when I last saw him, old and aging, without a childhood. The girls were stiff, they looked like they were going to start screaming at the top of their lungs. Harriet told me that practically everyone around us was on junk, or had tried it. I wasn't impressed.

We bought Pepsi-Cola and tried to talk above all the music. Harriet said she comes here every night. Harriet showed me a girl her age who was pregnant. Harriet said the superintendent in the building on 109th Street did it to her.

Harriet said her own baby is coming in less than seven months. She said she has her eye on a building on 83rd Street where two of her girlfriends are living with their babies. Harriet said she is sure she can get her own welfare case. I tried to tell Harriet that welfare would never allow her to live alone with a baby at her age. Harriet said, What does welfare care? I said to Harriet that she had to try and get rid of the baby because if she had the baby she would be on welfare for the rest of her life. No man would marry her if she had a baby and if she was a welfare case. I said she was going to ruin her whole life. I said if she got rid of the baby she could finish school, she could work and not have to be on welfare like Momma. Harriet said I didn't know what I was talking about. Harriet said welfare was money that you knew was coming in. The government sent it to you every two weeks. It was taxpayers money. We pay taxes, Harriet said, everybody pays taxes, we pay taxes on this Pepsi-Cola that we're drinking. I'm going to have my baby, Harriet said, and Momma can go to hell. She's dead already, Harriet said, Momma just doesn't know enough to lay down and die.

I couldn't talk Harriet out of the baby. She would live in the same kind of a room as Momma and be exactly like Momma and the more she hated Momma, the more she would be like Momma, until there would be no differences between them.

This is what I have seen happen to the girls in the building on 104th Street who had their own babies. They became exactly like their mothers as though they had been pressed by a big plate. Some even became worse than their mothers, because the only memory they have is of filth, while some of their mothers can still remember a life where there was a family, cousins, uncles, aunts, Sunday dinners, visiting, trips. Their mothers can remember a link, another human being, a person or persons to whom they belonged.

I belong to no one except to the memory of a father I have never seen and who has never seen me. What is he doing now, my father? Where does he live? What work does he do? Who does he see? Who is close to him? Does he have a family? Does he have any other children? Is he a man that I would want to be my father? I want my father to be a man who is not afraid. I want him to be proud. I want him to give me a part of his life. Would he be proud of me? Would my father accept me now as I am, if he would see me, if somehow the welfare investigators found him or Momma ran into him or if he came looking for Momma? Would I be the daughter of my father?

Our lives are so much bigger than we believe them to be.

To whom do all of the lives in the candy store belong? Where are the fathers for them?

Harriet's baby, if she has the baby, will never see the face of its father, because not even Harriet knows who the father is. What is a father? A father is the way out of all this welfare.

Because no father would let welfare be what it is. No father would let 104th Street stand. No father who worked would come home to West 104th Street. A father would tear the building down at its foundation and send it tumbling into the dust where it belongs.

Harriet said to me in the candy store that she was going to get some junk. She asked me if I wanted to watch. I said, No. I said she didn't have to take any dope. Harriet said a girl friend of hers had some and it would be free. I asked Harriet if she was still seeing men for money. Harriet said she had no other way of getting drugs. I told Harriet it would hurt her baby. Harriet said the baby would only come out hooked and the doctors could take care of that. Harriet said, Wait here and I'll be back in fifteen minutes. In fifteen minutes Harriet was back with the white stuff in her arms that was now in her blood that the baby inside of her was feeding on.

It was almost 11 o'clock. We started back for 104th Street.

Harriet said, Do you think Momma has had enough of that man? Harriet said to me, When are you going to start getting it?

I said I didn't want any babies.

Harriet said, I didn't want a baby either but now I've got one. My baby is too big now to kill.

The hallway had a bright light. The landlady keeps a 150 watts burning at night just as you get past the stoop. Three men were on the stoop drinking wine. One of them was Mr. G. from the 2nd floor who hasn't worked in 8 years. He was an elevator operator. He turned his ankle 8 years ago and had to stop working for three weeks. He didn't have money, so he went to welfare. Welfare opened a case for him and he has been on welfare ever since. I heard him tell the story to Momma. How days, then weeks, then months, then years went by and he was still on welfare and then he started crying to Momma saying he would never get off of welfare now and he would be like the rest of the drunks in the building. He is.

We knocked on the door. Momma said come in. She was alone in her bed. Momma said, What movie did you see? Harriet said we didn't go to the movies. Momma turned on her side and went back to sleep. Edgar was in our bed. He got up without crying when he saw me and Harriet.

Are we really brothers and sisters?

Edgar slept between us. He clutched me when we got into bed. His fingernails were almost digging into me. What had he seen between Momma and the new man?

There will only be a difference of three years between Edgar and Harriets baby, if she has her baby. What will Momma do when she begins to see the swelling? I didn't sleep. What was I doing in this room? What was anyone doing in this building who had babies, children? I wanted to push down the walls. I wanted to push down the ceiling to let in the sky.

What was I doing in this room? I heard the rats scratching in the walls. The rats seemed to be fighting with one another. They seemed to be fighting to get into our room. Maybe they smelled Edgar. Maybe they smelled Momma.

Then Momma screamed. I was cold and wet, my blood seemed to be rushing out of me. I couldn't move but I felt I had to rush up. Momma screamed again. I put on the light. Edgar was crying and screaming. Harriet sat up and looked more strange than anything else, with her face not knowing where she was at because of the drugs in her system.

I saw what had happened. A rat got loose from the wall and bit Momma. There were marks on her arm. She rushed to put her arm under the faucet. She kept the water running. She kept saying she had to wash the poison out. She soaped her arm. She had me pour rubbing alcohol on her arm. The teeth marks were big. The rat had bitten deep. I said to Momma that she should go to the emergency clinic at St. Lukes. Not now, Momma said, in the morning. I can't go now, she kept saying.

I said the teeth marks were deep. I said rats carry a lot of poison in their teeth. Momma looked at her arm again and said she thought she had better go. It was almost light outside. Momma put on her dress and a coat. She said she would take a taxi to St. Lukes.

I no longer believe even this will make Momma move and I must have my own plans, if I can.

January 30

A rat exterminator went through the building.

January 31

Momma keeps looking at the bite marks on her arm as though trying to read a meaning into the marks. We sleep with the light on now. Momma is up half of the night. When she hears a noise she throws a shoe against the wall. With the light on I read until I fall asleep. It is the only way I can get to sleep.

Harriet is beginning to show. I can see a slight swelling of her stomach. I tell Harriet that she has to see a doctor. But Harriet says she will be thrown out of school if they find out she is pregnant and she doesn't want to spend all day hanging around 104th Street.

February 1

Momma asked me if I talked to any of the boys at school. I said some.

February 2

H.L. sits two seats away from me in English. Most of the time he seems to be staring out of the window. But when the teacher calls on him he always knows the answer. Today he knew the name of the first American to get a Nobel Prize for writing books.

February 3

H.L. was talking to the college adviser when I went down at 2 o'clock. Later he said to me, Are you thinking of going to college?

I said, If I can.

H.L. said, My father says if he can make payments on a Dodge he can make college payments for me. He says I'll be running longer than a Dodge.

February 5

H.L. is tall. He always wears a white shirt.

February 7

H.L. brushed against me when we were going into class. I felt my breasts get hard. My nipples stuck out. Do I like H.L. that much?

February 9

H.L. wasn't in class for two days.

February 10

In the toilet at school C.M. and P.K. started laughing when I came in. He got it, they said, he got busted. He got it even if he could talk up in class.

Busted for what? I said. Did he only stick his d. in you, nothing else? They laughed again. The girls started jabbing their arms.

The drug disease got to H.L. too. The drug disease is in the air. You can breathe it in the school. You can breathe the drugs in the hallways, in the toilets, in the subway cars, in the cafeteria. It is a disease that doesn't care who its victims are. The drug disease enters every classroom. But what made H.L. do it? Nobody will ever be able to tell me. He won't be back in class, not after this. He is gone. They will put him in jail like they used to chain mental patients to the wall.

February 11

Tonight in bed while Harriet was sleeping, she put her arms around me. She put one of her hands on my stomach. One of her hands was between my legs. I wanted H.L.s hands there. H.L. started something in me. Something that Harriet knows better than me. I wanted H.L. to kiss me. I wanted him to touch my breasts. I wanted him to keep kissing me. I wanted him to look at me when I came into class.

Now I know how I want it to be when I marry. I want a big bed. I want the whitest sheets. I want my husband to touch me with hands that feel like the hands of God when he created the world. I want him in me deeper than I can imagine anything to be. A deepness like the sky which doesn't have any end. That kind of deepness. The deepness of billions and billions of stars, billions of stars beyond them. That kind of deepness must be the deepness you must feel with a man. Sometimes at night that deepness comes to me. But I never see the face of the man who is in me. I never know the man. I never know who is in me touching parts of me that I can never reach. When it happens at night I sometimes cry out like Momma does. But my cries can't be heard. Mommas cries I can hear. Does it give Momma pleasure? I don't think its supposed to be pleasure. When it happens, when my body trembles, it is because I am witness to the beginnings of the world. I see the whole world in formation. I see mountains rising up, rivers forming, oceans swelling, valleys opening, all life bursting into existence.

February 13

Harriet was sick this morning. Momma didn't guess why.

February 15

A new investigator was over today. He told Momma that she had to move as though he was making a great proclamation. He said the building was no place to raise children. He said we needed three bedrooms, so that the children could have some privacy. He said Edgars asthma was probably psychological because he had no room to breathe. Momma just stared at him and nodded what looked like yes. But none of the words got through to her. The investigator was talking to hear himself say words that made him feel good. *He was doing something.*

I never saw an investigator who came to see us who knew what their job should be. Their job should be to cry out to the heavens that this building stinks, that the landlord and landlady are evil people no matter how nice they try to be, that welfare is rotten as long as it makes people rotten, that welfare kills and destroys human life, its as though 5000 babies are being burned alive every week. This is what an investigator should do. And not ask their stupid questions. And not pretend they are *sympathetic*. One cannot be sympathetic to the way we live. One can only hate it. Hate it. Hate it. Hate it.

February 16

Harriet has been out of school three days. She stays in bed. Momma wanted to call a welfare doctor but Harriet said no. Harriet leaves the room once a day to get a shot of heroin. She tells me she would tremble and shake if she didn't get the needle in her arm. I cannot believe that Harriet is so used to the drugs. I expect her at any minute to start smiling and say it was all a play she had invented.

February 18

My birthday is never celebrated but I was born on this day.

February 23

Mommas arm has been swelling. She went to the St. Lukes emergency room. The only family doctor we have is the emergency room.

February 25

Harriet told me that she can no longer hide the fact that she is pregnant from Momma. She said that Momma will notice it any day now. Harriet said there is a boy she knows who has a room on 84th Street and she can stay there. She said that if she stays in our room Momma will probably beat her to death.

Harriet is right. But it doesnt make it any more right to live in a room on West 84th Street with a boy who is also on drugs. I told Harriet she shouldnt run away.

Harriet said she wouldnt run away like Charles. We would always know where she was at. She said the boy had a room with a bath in it. She said she could take a bath or a shower. She said there were no cockroaches in the room. She said there was space for a kitchen table and he had 4 chairs. She said his bed had clean sheets, which the building changed once a week.

I asked Harriet if the boy knew she was going to have a baby. She said, He knows. He will only let her stay for a couple of weeks, maybe a month.

Then what? I asked Harriet.

I can go into a girls home to have the baby, Harriet said, and when I come out with my baby I can have my own welfare case.

You can't at 14 years of age, I almost yelled at Harriet.

Harriet said when she has the baby she will be over 15 years old and that would be old enough for her to get her own welfare check.

February 26

I received 637 out of 800 points on the English Achievement test. Miss A. said it was a fine mark. Momma said it's better than 636.

February 27

I asked the landlady today if every person in this building was on welfare. She said, No my dear, there is a man on the second floor with Social Security payments.

March 4

Mommas arm is still swollen. She says the doctors at St. Lukes cant tell her what is wrong. She takes pills to keep any infection from spreading. Momma spends most of her time in bed. She doesnt read, she doesnt listen to the radio or watch TV. Nobody comes to visit her. She doesnt play with Edgar. She doesnt look at Harriet. I think a fever keeps her in bed.

The rats used to carry the plague that gave fevers that I read about in history, the bubonic plague. But we don't have plagues today in the cities. We may have dope addicts who rob from the poor, we may have thousands of people on welfare in just these few blocks off Central Park West, we may have every room and every apartment on this street robbed at least once, we may have schools that dont teach, we may have teachers who are frightened of their students, we may have buildings that stink like this one, we may have children on drugs, but we don't have the bubonic plague. What is the plague over us? Why can't we see the plague? Why can't we fight the plague over our heads? Why doesnt anyone take up arms? Why dont we hear bugles blowing every day calling out people to fight the plague of drugs, housing, the schools, welfare? They should be blowing from every rooftop in New York.

But I only hear silence. It is the strangest silence. It is as though everyone is blind, walking without a stick tapping their way. I can't cry loud enough. I cant even scream loud enough for Momma to hear me.

This has been my life so far. Silence. I want to be heard from. I would love to be able to hate. Like Momma. If Momma could hate we would not have lived here for a single day. How does one learn how to hate? Who should I begin hating first? The landlady of this building? She isn't my enemy. She sits and takes money for these rooms because "somebody" has to be the landlord of these buildings. Should I hate my teachers? Some of them just graduated from college and they have only learned how to hate, not to teach. I cant blame them for hating because they are teaching children who dont believe that any kind of knowledge is for them. Should I hate the police? They only do a job. Who is it I should hate? Should I hate Momma? Momma knows welfare has broken her back as though a truck rolled over it but she doesnt know why welfare has broken her. Welfare makes you forget there is a tomorrow. Most other people live in tomorrows. Their days are never finished. Each day is a beginning. There is always work for them to do. Work must be beautiful. I think Momma could be made beautiful again if only she could find work that would take her out of welfare and into the bright open world. You never hear about rats biting people who go to work each day. Momma must be able to find some kind of work. I cant hate Momma. She is the only person in the world that I am linked to. I have no one to hate, yet I feel I should hate everyone and everything.

The welfare doctor came today to look at Mommas arm. He came very soon after I called Mommas investigator and told him that Momma needed a doctor. The welfare people are very quick to send doctors to your house. They don't want anyone on welfare to die because a doctor couldnt get to them. Then it would make welfare look bad. The doctor said Momma had a temperature and said she should stay in bed, if she could.

I see Momma in her bed. She lays flat on her back. She stares up at the ceiling. The light bulb doesn't seem to bother her. It is as though the light bulb is protection from a thousand dangers. Does Momma know what her life is? Does she recognize herself in that light that shines on all of us when we see ourself as we know ourselves to be? When we become so alive to all color, all sounds, to movement, to voices, to shapes, to the form of things, that every object looks pure to us and we feel ourselves pure. It is this purity that I long for. It is this purity that every mother should have and which I think most mothers do have, for it permits them to see their children in their inner life.

But Momma didn't see Charles this way. She hasn't seen Harriet, Edgar or myself. What Momma has is some kind of a useless wasted strength that permits her to survive in this room, in this building, on 104th Street. Wasted strength is what all of the mothers in this building have. Each one of them that I know wastes their strength on failure. They have kept their children alive. This seems to be their supreme achievement. Only very occasionally is a baby found murdered. Only occasionally is a baby thrown from a roof on 104th Street or found in a basement. The welfare babies live. And when the welfare babies get old enough to be approached by life they are scattered like dry leaves and blown away from life.

March 5

I went from 104th Street up Amsterdam Avenue past the Cathedral of St. John the Divine which looked closed. I walked past St. Lukes Hospital where Momma always takes Edgar for emergencies until I came to Columbia University. That is the route I planned for myself today. The university is so big. The buildings look stiff and cold like the apartment buildings on Central Park West. But the students all looked busy as they hurried across the walks to their classrooms. I walked with them. And felt myself walking as fast as they were to their classrooms.

Columbia University seems to be on top of a hill, on a height, high above 104th Street. Do the teachers at Columbia sometimes leave 116th Street, do they know the West Side streets that their students will probably never know except through a few books? You need to know so much to be at Columbia. Why don't the teachers go into the streets below the university?

The teachers should be talking to Momma. They should be teaching her how to live in a world that Momma seems to have stumbled in without knowing her way. There is nobody for Momma to learn from. I walked to Columbia University to be away from 104th Street for a while. I wouldn't want to go to Columbia. I want to go to a college where there are tall trees, grass, houses with white fences around them, a graceful river, white swans, classrooms full of sunlight, fresh clean air. No matter how smart the teachers are at Columbia they all breathe the same dirty air I breathe.

March 15

Momma is out of bed. The swelling on her arm has gone away.

March 21

Harriet is in St. Lukes Hospital. Blood started coming down her legs. Momma and me rushed her to the emergency at St. Lukes. We left Edgar with a neighbor. Momma learned in the emergency room that Harriet was pregnant and that she lost her baby when the blood started gushing out. Momma also learned Harriet is on drugs. Momma just sat in the emergency clinic and didn't say a word. The doctors said Harriet was a very sick girl and the first thing was to "dry her out." We took a taxi back to 104th Street. Momma had trouble getting up the stairs. Mr. D. who is always drunk was coming down the stairs. He stopped to put his hand on my shoulder. Momma suddenly screamed at him, Take your dirty hands off of her! Mr. D. backed away, with a frightened look on his face, like a dog that puts its tail between its legs.

Momma opened the door to our room and stood in the doorway staring at the room. She saw what I did. The light bulb still burning. A pile of dirty clothes near the sink. Dishes piled in the sink. An open box of corn flakes on the table. The two beds against the walls that filled the room. The dirty green walls. The cracked plaster. The hole in the ceiling where we nailed a flattened tin can to keep out the rats. The television set still on showing Indians chasing a stage coach across a western desert. We ran out of the room with Harriet and didn't stop to turn off the set. Momma stared at the TV set from the doorway. The Indians were being shot down by the people inside of the stage coach. One Indian jumped on the stage coach. The program changed to a commercial. Momma stared at the commercial. It was a commercial with a man singing in a vineyard and then showing bottles of wine.

I stood alongside Momma. I was hoping she would slam the door to the room and not enter it. We would go with only our bodies and the clothes on our back to the welfare office and demand they find us a place where we could live. With all the millions of dollars they had to spend they could find us a place. We would never come back to 104th Street. Whatever we owned would stay in the room. It would be buried in the room, the dead clothes, the dead pots and pans, the dead food. We didn't need any of it. We had to start life. We had to make the move toward life. Certainly Momma felt this standing in the doorway even if she didn't speak. We had to go like the people who landed on the shores of America, like the immigrants who immediately threw off everything of their past life except the desire to make a new world. We could do it. We could close the door. We could never enter this room again. We could go back down the steps past the landlady without looking at her.

I could feel my lips trembling. I said to Momma, Let's close the door to this room and not go into it. Let's not go into it. If we have to, we'll sleep on the sidewalk tonight. By tomorrow we should have a new room. Let's just do it.

Momma crossed into the room without answering me. It seemed impossible to me to enter the room. My feet wouldn't take me over the doorway.

Momma said, What are you standing there for?

I was waiting for a miracle. When none came, I entered the room and then went to pick up Edgar.

March 29

Harriet is home from St. Lukes Hospital. Momma is calm toward Harriet. There has been no screaming. During all the time Harriet was in the hospital, Momma never mentioned Harriet to me. But I could see Mommas eyes and mind working and maybe Momma knew Harriet was the last person to blame.

April 5

Harriet told me that she must change schools. The girls who still take the drugs are after her to start again. Harriet said one of them put a knife up against her chest in the toilet at school. Harriet said she was warned that she would be stabbed the next time.

April 10

Harriet said she keeps stalling the girls by saying her blood is weak after losing her baby. She said she tells the girls that she may die if she starts taking the drugs again. I asked Harriet if I could talk to the girls. Harriet said no one can talk to them. They have their rules and that is the way they live. They won't listen to me or anybody else.

April 14

Harriet said the girls gave her a month, and then she must start taking drugs again.

April 22

I feel as though Momma, Harriet, Edgar and myself are now racing a time clock that may mean the end of us all if we don't get away from here before the time clock of our lives explodes. I feel our lives speeding up. We can't stay in this building longer than it takes to move. At night there are shrieks and screams from 104th Street and we no longer can tell if it is a life in danger or if its only a drunk screaming.

I am now afraid to go out at night to the library. For three nights men have followed me down West 104th Street. One of them tried to grab me but a squad car came by. Any person who doesn't know what is happening on these sidewalks and who walks here alone at night gets robbed or mugged. A doctor was stabbed on the corner of 103rd Street and Central Park West. The robbing now is more open because nobody dares to see what is happening. I heard Momma say its safer to stay awake at night and sleep during the day. In the houses across the street they just kick open the doors and take what they want. I don't think stealing like this from people ever happened before in America.

It can't be welfare that causes all of this stealing, the drug addicts, the screaming. The welfare people lay in their dirty rooms. The welfare people are the victims, not the doers. But it is the welfare money that is the cause. The welfare money makes you feel you are getting something for nothing, even though you need the money to stay alive. It is this feeling of something for nothing that fills 104th Street and all of the blocks down the West Side that I know. All the people here are haunted by knowing they are not living like other people.

April 25

Miss A. told me today she might go back to college. She said there is a lot more that she feels she can learn. Miss A. said there is so much to be taught. Miss A. said there is so much to unlearn. Miss A. said we would always keep in touch. She didn't speak to me today like a teacher to a pupil. It was almost like a friend to a friend. There was a sound of good-bye, to, in her voice, as though this school will never see her again. It will be a good school that gets Miss A.

April 28

It is 8 o'clock. Momma is watching the TV set. Harriet is watching the door as though somebody will kick it in. Edgar is playing on the floor. I am sitting by the table. I am not going to write in this diary again until my graduation from school. It is only two months away. For two months I will pretend that 104th Street doesn't exist. I will pretend that I am living suspended in time, like an ancient princess in the *Arabian Nights*. I will write nothing in these pages. They will be blank. I do not want to see what is on 104th Street any more. I have seen enough. The blank pages may be the best pages in this diary. The blank pages will reveal that I can keep my distance from 104th Street. I do not breathe its air of failure. This is the welfare sickness. Failure. To be able to live with failure. And not even to know this is what is happening. It may be all that Momma wants from life now.

It may be all that Harriet expects now from life. It may be what Edgar has already learned of life.

I will run from this failure. I will outrun it for all the days of my life. It will never be faster than me. I will be swifter than it and always keep it at my back. It will never get ahead of me. I don't know what I will be running toward but I do know that I will be running from failure, and that I will see West 104th Street as a life that is not worthy of existence. But I do not want to forget Momma, because she is all that I have to link me to the beginning of my way into the world. And now to close the book.

June 28

I have graduated. I have scholarships from two colleges. I am taking the one that will take me away from New York. I will have enough money for school and to pay for room and board. It is almost like being on welfare but with all of the difference in the world.

Momma will not be able to stay forever on 104th Street. The building will be torn down one day. I would like to see the bulldozers smashing at it, the big ball of steel hurling against its walls. Nothing will be saved from 104th Street. The wreckers will smash it to the ground, into dust. I wish the wreckers could go to work on welfare, smashing it with their balls of steel, their bulldozers, breaking down its walls, making it possible for millions of lives to be in a sunlight always hidden from them.

Momma said to me that she will ask the investigator if I can get money from welfare to pay for the train to the college in Ohio.

I told Momma wherever there was a job for me in New York I would find it and I would work and pay for the train to Ohio.

For a moment I thought I saw Momma smile with a pride that I always wanted to see on her face.

I love Momma. I love Harriet. I love Edgar. I must never forget they are my family. Even if the world has tried to make us forget.